CIDER APPLES

THE NEW POMONA

By Liz Copas
2013

*With Cider apples from all the cider growing counties;
Somerset, Devon, Dorset, Cornwall, Gloucestershire, Hereford
and Worcester. Including the new 21st century cider apples*

IN PRAISE OF CIDER . . .

Cider of the finest quality, is a rich white wine, only second to the best juice of the grape. Cider of this quality can only be made in special seasons from special fruit; just as the finest wines, called 'vintage' wines, can only be produced in rare seasons. Cider making is not so old an industry as grape wine making, because to make a wine you have only to jump into a basket of ripe grapes and dance about till the juice runs out, keep the must or juice for a week to ferment, and then you can get as drunk as Noah in no time. Apples require machinery to crush them and press the juice out, and altogether demand more mechanical and modern lines of thought and treatment than grapes. But that a good pleasant drink can be made from apples is unquestionable.

Proceedings of the Mid-Somerset Agricultural Society's
first Cider Conference, Shepton Mallet, 1903

© Tithe map of Merriott
Somerset Archives and Local Services

ISBN 978-0-9568994-2-2

Printed in Great Britain by
Short Run Press Ltd, Exeter

CONTENTS

PREFACE

Like many people who used to work at Long Ashton, Liz Copas has boundless enthusiasm for cider apples and orchards. You only have to mention Long Ashton and people's eyes light up. It was the nerve centre of the Cider Industry from top to bottom, whether you were a large producer in Somerset and Hereford or a small farmer tucked away in Cornwall or West Dorset you went along to the tastings and consulted the specialists about your apples and your cider making. Maybe you needed your juice analysing or apples identifying or the latest bug destroying or disease investigated. The knowledge that was built up at Long Ashton since it was started in 1903 was diverse, wonderful and very, very useful. It provided the backbone to the industry and some of the Professors like Professor Barker were often revered as Local Gods.

Long Ashton not only made outstanding cider and perry, they had laboratories and trial orchards dotted all over the south west and were often thinking twenty, thirty or even fifty years ahead with new varieties or envisaging future problems. Sadly Long Ashton was closed down in 2003 when the 100 year lease ran out and the land sold off for development.

Ironically with the new wave of cider makers and the prospect of climate change, and new diseases, we need Long Ashton now, more than ever. The knowledge built up by those that worked at Long Ashton was invaluable, and now that the numbers of those that worked there is dwindling, it is vital that they hand on their knowledge either person to person through workshops or talks or here in book form, or else it is lost forever.

Liz Copas, who was the last pomologist at Long Ashton, worked there for over twenty years. She has been freelance for another ten years and has helped the industry enormously, not least through the National Association of Cider Makers with fruit trials and in developing new varieties known as the 'Girls'. She has also undertaken some very valuable work helping to identify over two dozen 'new' and old cider apples in Dorset. The publication of her first book *Somerset Pomona* in 1999 was a landmark in the cider world – it was an instant success. It sold out fast and despite several reprints, many apple entrepreneurs have bemoaned its disappearance from the book shelves. Wait no more. Here is a re-vamped enlarged edition which conveniently spreads over into the adjoining counties that make up Ciderland, an area of South West England that is now positively bulging with new and adventurous cider makers and new orchards.

But the cider maker, whether newly fledged or long in the tooth, is only as good as their fruit. None of this 'concentrate' malarkey. One likes to see the orchards, not an empty tin can or plastic bucket. But to understand the orchards the cidermaker has to know each variety almost as if they were their own relations, for their livelihood and reputation depends on it.

This new book, *Cider Apples – The New Pomona* should be on the shelves of every self respecting cider maker and orchardist from Land's End to John o'Groats . . . and before you ask : Yes they are making cider in Scotland even Norway. And apples do grow in Iceland. So I can heartily recommend this book and hope you will devour its knowledge and that it will inspire you not only to plant more orchards with local varieties but to experiment with cider making. And then the ancient regional tastes of cider will become once more a pure joy for the itinerant traveller. There is no real point for the small cidermaker to try and make a cider that tastes the same year in year out. That is the preserve of the industrial scale cider makers who do play a really important role in satisfying the mass market.

What really interests me is the emergence of new niche markets that even in the last ten years have blossomed, even grown exponentially, and will showcase new regional tastes and flavours. That is really exciting and a wonderful prospect. Not just county by county, but valley by valley and village by village. The secret of making a full bodied, rounded, deep, long lasting cider is often in the tannins and terroir, orchards and soils, local climate and a little secret 'know how' which all cider makers keep tucked up their sleeve.

This book tells you all you need to know about South West Cider Apples and is a brilliant starting point for anyone thinking of planting an orchard and entering that magical world of cider and apples.

We should all be grateful to Liz Copas for sharing her knowledge of apples and orchards so generously over the years. Professor Barker would have been very proud to know that the knowledge from Long Ashton is still being used and like the trees themselves, propagated very widely.

James Crowden

INTRODUCTION

Since the *Somerset Pomona* has been out of print now for quite a few years, I thought it high time that it was updated for a new version. So much has happened in the cider world since 1999 when the first edition was published. Cider has firmly established itself as number one drink, it is advertised on telly, all the supermarkets stock shelves of it and every other village in the West Country has at least one artisan cidermaker and more than one annual cider festival.

The Royal Bath & West Show's Cider Competition has done much to revive interest in cider making. There were over 500 entries in this year's 2013 Show, in all classes from traditional cloudy farmhouse cider to bottle conditioned sparkling cider, and they came with every conceivable flavour and character. The standard of amateur cidermaking has risen exponentially over the last decade and most entries were very good to excellent.

The continued success of our ciders depends so much on the raw material, cider apples. We have many, many different varieties to choose from, some well tried and tested, some in a vintage class, others only mediocre and yet more to be re-discovered tucked away in the corners of fields, gardens and in our old farm orchards. It is my aim here to describe as best I can the merits of a wide range of apples that the average hunter-gatherer cidermaker might be able to find, and give a little help in identifying them.

The scope has widened. Some of the hard-to-find ancient varieties that were included in the comprehensive first editions have been replaced by a range of varieties from further west; Dorset, Devon and Cornwall. Cidermaking traditions in those counties are very different from Somerset and the West Midlands. Farm orchards in the west had to be versatile, to provide fruit for eating and cooking as well as for cider. Many Devon and Cornish varieties are dual or even treble purpose apples, fair to middling for all three uses. It is these varieties that change the local character of cider the further you travel west away from the bittersweets of Somerset. But regional distinctiveness is important and a quality to be preserved by local cidermakers, even if not fully appreciated by all customers.

So you will see a number of those sorts of varieties included here, many of them well known household names, but all making an essential contribution to present day artisan cidermaking. And also, for those who are seriously considering new orchards, a full list of the new Long Ashton cider apples, The Girls.

My thanks go to many friends and members of the South West of England Cidermakers Association, Orchards Live, the South West Fruit Group and others who have helped me collate this edition. Special thanks to Thatchers Cider for use of their invaluable apple tree collection, Chris Groves who looks after the Cornish tree collection at NT Cothele, James and Mary Evans the Cornish cider apple experts, Vernon Shutler of Countryman Cider for all the local apples he found for me and to Kevin Croucher at Thornhayes nursery.

Liz Copas
Somerset 2013

Getting To Know Cider Apples

WILD CRABS, CODLINS AND REINETTES

Wild apple trees flourish here in the West Country. The small round yellow-green fruits of *Malus sylvestris* have the strongest combination of acidity and astringent tannin that any cidermaker could wish for. Although there is no archaeological evidence that Neolithic Brits drank cider, they certainly ate wild apples. Bronze Age shards and apple pips from the remains of wild apple trees have been excavated from around old settlements. It is easy to imagine that sometimes the apples would have fermented naturally after prolonged storage and that the sampling of the liquid product must have occurred. Appreciation of the intoxicating effects would surely have encouraged the samplers to repeat and refine the process and pass on the secret to friends and neighbours.

But it is said, that like so many other good things, the Romans brought proper apples and cider to Britain. Certainly they brought their propagation techniques of grafting and budding, thus opening the door for experiments in improving the raw material needed for a more palatable drink. In addition they brought their own apple varieties, although not all would have thrived in the higher latitude. Some of them would have had a dash of another wild crab, *Malus pumila*, with a new range of flavours and tannins.

Possibly even before the Romans, other travellers from the Mediterranean to our western shores may have brought some with Kazakh blood from *M.sieversii*, as we now call it, or the red fleshed crab *M. pumila var. niedzwetskyana*, since traffic from Asia Minor through the fertile crescent was well established before then. Both these apple species have rich and varied tannins. Later still the

Normans brought over some of their apple varieties and by the 13th century when cidermaking was a widespread pursuit, codlins, custards and reinettes came to our orchards. All our present-day apples, eaters, cookers and ciders, come from these common origins – the wild crabs.

THE BITTER AND THE SWEET

After centuries of selection and cultivation by man, we have literally thousands of apples for every purpose to choose from, all shapes and sizes, large and small, all shades of green-red-yellow and many different flavours.

Any apple will make cider but to make good cider you need to get to know your apples. There are usually plenty of cooking apples going begging every autumn. Some make excellent cider but most are just too acidic to make drinkable cider on their own. The quality of a cooking apple is often judged by the ease with which it will cook to a pulp, the frothier the better, and it is their acid component that achieves this. Eating apples make only fair cookers since they do not have enough acidity to do more than soften on cooking, but remain firmly in shape, although they can add interesting texture and colour. Fresh dessert apples are pleasant to the palate, not excessively sweet nor too sharp, but sub-acid, that agreeable in-between with enough character to accentuate the flavour and get the taste buds going but with just enough sugar to mask the sharpness. You can make cider with both cookers and eaters but there will always be something missing. The sharpness will still be there after the sugar is fermented but the cider will be thin, always pale coloured, rather sour, often lacking flavour and with no memorable after-taste that lingers on the tongue and exercises the taste buds.

True West Country bittersweet cider apples however have several extra qualities. Selected by cidermakers over the centuries and cherished in farm orchards, they are purpose grown solely for making the very best of traditional ciders. They will have plenty of tannin, sugar to ferment and just a little acid to balance the juice.

Bittersweet cider apples are closest to their wild ancestors. Their juice retains some of the natural tannins and their taste is astringent and at first unpalatable. Tannins, complex phenolic molecules, evolved in ancestral malus species as part of their natural plant defence mechanisms. When the skin of an apple is broken, say by insect damage, the juice flows and is exposed to the air. Phenolic compounds are easily oxidised and the flesh quickly turns brown. The thick brown oxidised juice, blocks and closes the wound, in much the same way that blood clots to seal a cut, and the fruit is protected from further damage. Some of these compounds are strongly fungistatic, that is, they discourage the growth of fungal diseases that attack apple trees.

The quality bittersweet taste comes from a selection of many complex molecules that subtly change during the mysterious process of fermentation to create 'body', 'mouthfeel' and the unique colour and flavours of real cider. There is plenty of information available on the complexities of tannins but it is not essential to make an in-depth study of them to become an expert on selecting the best apples. Suffice to say here, there are two main characters to look for; astringency and bitterness, and the best way to judge the tannin qualities of the apples you chose, is to taste them. With practice it soon becomes possible to differentiate between the mouth-drawing sensation of astringency and a more tongue-furring bitter taste. The tannic constituents of some apples are gentle and soft, like the excellent bittersweet Dabinett. In others like Chisel Jersey, they may be strong and harsh. These sorts are best blended with more desirably flavoured apples. Harsh tannin is useful for extending a juice made with poor quality fruit or a large proportion of dessert or culinary apples. Learn to appreciate the quality of the tannin in your fruit to suit your purpose.

Apples that combine tannin with some acidity are known as bittersharps and like the bittersweet apples they have more than 0.2% tannin. Bittersharps are more peculiar to south and central Somerset where some excellent varieties of character have originated, such as the legendary Kingston Black and the exceptional Stoke Red. In a good year they can produce a cider with a pleasing balance of bitterness, acidity and sweetness, alone without blending. There are others, like Porters Perfection, a rather sharp selection from Porter's nursery in Lambrook. The closely related Stembridge Clusters and Lambrook Pippin also once had some local reputation. The cider of some of the more acidic bittersharps is often improved by a gentle, natural malo-lactic fermentation in the following spring.

Not all cider apples are rich in tannin. Some have little or no tannin, just flavour and sugar. These are termed sweets or pure sweets. The well known and much loved Morgan Sweet is a pure sweet as are Taylor's Sweet, Dunkerton's Late, Woodbine and many others. On their own they make a thin but interesting cider and are usually best blended with bittersweets.

Cider apples rich in malic acid, more than 0.45%, but low or lacking in tannin are classed as sharps. True cider sharps, selected, valued and cherished, like Gin or Backwell Red and Black Vallis, natives of north Somerset or Browns Apple from Devon, have special 'vintage' qualities to raise the drink out of the ordinary. But our farm orchards also contain a motley collection of cooking and eating apples, together with those useful varieties loosely termed, dual purpose. These sorts are generally quite sharp, with from 0.45-0.8% or even 1.0% acidity. Their sharpness is culinary in its character, rather than vintage quality, a difference difficult to describe without tasting a few apples to compare the flavours. They are traditionally multi-purpose, being suitable for cooking early in the season, then for eating as the acidity mellows with keeping and finally, when they are no longer fit for the kitchen, ready for the cider press. Names like Tom Putt, Crimson King and the ancient variety Stubbard have lived in old orchards and contributed to farm cider for centuries.

True cider apples have yet another unique property, their texture. They are not crisp or crunchy to the bite. They are woolly and everlastingly chewy as anyone who tries to eat one will discover. The farmers of the old days were clever enough to appreciate this woolly-ness as a virtue, for it boosts apple press-ability enormously. Even in modern pressing mills with heavy hydraulic equipment, apples like Cox and Bramley are very slippery and difficult to press efficiently. Their arrival at the cider press is greeted with groans. Whatever the method of extraction, woolly textured cider apples are more stable and yield greater quantities of juice. Centuries of horse-powered stone crushing must have led to this piece of evolution by selection of the most manageable under difficult conditions.

REGIONAL TASTES AND FLAVOURS

Somerset has a well preserved tradition for growing good bittersweets and the majority of its native apples fall into this category. Traditional Somerset cider therefore has a strong tannic character, some astringency and perhaps a little lingering bitterness on the back of the tongue. Herefordshire cider's time-honoured character is similarly bittersweet, perhaps even more so than Somerset's. Old records from the 17th and 18th centuries [Hogg 1886] suggest there was much interest in the flavour and colour of the juice and that, with favourite apples, the tannin content of the juice was particularly important, possibly more so than the sugar content and even the alcoholic potential. For Hereford and much of Somerset, farm cidermaking was a serious business, the loyalty of the farm workforce depending very much on the quality of the cider offered in part for wages. The best cider attracted the best workers and a reputation for poor cider soon got around to the bands of itinerant workers essential for sheep shearing and haymaking.

Regional tastes change as you travel southwards and the further you go the necessity for palpable tannin seems to wane, the taste gets sharper and the colour of the cider pales. In the late 1930s a scientist was dispatched from the Cider

Institute to visit various cider and cheese makers in Dorset with the intention of 'improving' both farm products and raising them to the Institute's good standards. He did not spend long in the county having found only a few areas of Dorset suitable for growing trees productively, but he did make a short list of the native cider apple varieties that he found in the south west corner of the county. Interestingly only one or two are bittersweets, such as Golden Bittersweet, but most of the apples he found have little tannin and fall into either the sharp class, such as the excellent Golden Ball and Kings Favourite, or are just plain dual purpose suitable for the limited resources of small, often tenant farms needing adaptability from their fruit. In Dorset, Buttery Dor and the well known Tom Putt come into this category.

In Devon and spilling over the border into Somerset, locally bred sharps are quite common in the old orchards and have a significant influence on the characteristic, more acidic flavour of Devon cider, often described as 'dry' by those who dislike a really sour taste. Few of the native Devon apples can boast of a true bittersweet juice. There are many pure sharps, those with a high acid content but with a good 'cider' flavour lacking any culinary overtones. Coleman's seedling, Fair Maid of Devon and the excellent Browns Apple are typical examples. Often pure sharps are quite low in sugar and need to be supplemented to boost the fermentation. In Devon, pure sweet apples fill this role, varieties such as Northwood, Slack-ma-Girdle and Tale Sweet. They lack tannin and have only moderate acidity but often give a distinctive flavour and aroma to the cider. In Devon it is these two types of varieties, sharps and sweets, that should be commonly found in the orchards that belonged to good local cidermakers. Many years ago there were certainly some cider connoisseurs in the corner of Devon that stretches from Totnes round to Plymouth. One or two superior cider varieties hail from there, most probably cherished seedlings raised by cidermakers searching for improvements. The very old variety, Tan or Teign Harvey from Teignmouth, a bittersharp and the full bittersweet Kingston Bitter, are relatively recent re-discoveries from South Hams. There was and still is plenty of competition in that part of the world where small-scale cidermakers abound. But the bigger companies also did their bit. In the early 20th century Whiteways Cider Company north of Exeter was responsible for collecting and growing the best of the Devon cider varieties in their orchards at Whimple, together with many vintage varieties from Somerset and Hereford. They even had a selection of cider apples from France as recommended by the Cider Institute. Many of these were varieties collected by Robert Neville-Grenville and the Bulmer family, whose experimental French collections were well known at the turn into the 20th century. There is also a hot-spot of orchards on the good soils around Crediton that still hang on to some of the best Devon varieties. In their time, the cider from those apples must have been exceptional. But so many of the old farm orchards in Devon and Cornwall, like those in Dorset, hedged their bets by growing predominantly dual purpose fruit and making the best cider out of whatever they could.

The last real outpost for cider apples was the Tamar Valley, a sheltered spot with a favoured climate, although more orchards have been planted further westward in more recent times. Even here most of the varieties are dual purpose with the exception of the enigmatic vintage bittersharp Dufflin, perhaps still too sharp for some but with a superior reputation going back to the 19th century.

Regional preferences still exist to some extent for farmhouse ciders and local customers will make their criticism if the product falls short of their expectations. But these days there are so many and varied ciders available at farms and on the shop shelves that aficionados will have developed appreciation for many and varied styles and tastes. Such customer awareness allows more freedom than has have ever been known for those with a little imagination to create their own ciders with elegance and flair.

SEEDLINGS, PITCHERS, BURR KNOTS AND GRIBBLES

Although most of our cider apples are not much more than one or two hundred years old, there are a few which are clearly ancient, 17th century or before. Stubbard is one, a codlin type, closely resembling a wild apple. The name Stubbard may have originated from 'stub' or 'stump', referring to their ability, in common with many truly old apples, to root from cuttings. Sometimes they are also called 'pitchers', trees whose trunks and limbs bear lumps and bumps from which roots arise when 'cuttings' [usually quite large pieces of branch] are 'pitched' into the ground. Captain Broad, a big fruited codlin apple from Cornwall, is another pitcher that roots from a cutting with burr knots.

Most cooking and table apple varieties would once have been grafted onto a 'free' or seedling stock until the 16th century, when the Paradise rootstock, a *Malus pumila* hybrid, was introduced from Europe to encourage faster cropping. It is unlikely though that it would have been used on cider apples until probably the 20th century. It was common practice to grow seedlings from pomace left from the apple pressing. Both stocks and new trees with potential for fruit would have been selected from any promising seedlings that arose. Royal Wildling is one of ancient origin. Dabinett and Yarlington Mill are more recent 'gribbles', wildling or gribble being other names for a seedling.

John Garland, gardener at Killerton House in Devon, wrote in *Apple Culture in Devon* in the late 18th century . . .

'The seeds or pips are generally obtained from the pressed pulp after the cider has been extracted. The pulp is beaten up, spread in an open, airy loft and kept regularly turned until it is sufficiently dry for the pips to be sifted out. Early in spring the seed should be sown on well-prepared land, such as has been manured, dug and exposed to the action of the winter frosts, the ground being forked over and got into a fine, or well-pulverized condition.

Beds are marked off 3 to 4 feet wide, leaving a 2 feet alley between. The seed is evenly, but not too thickly sown on the beds and covered with soil taken from the alleys. From the time the seed is sown until the young plants are above the ground, the beds must be well-guarded from the depredations of mice.

The young plants which are locally termed gribbles, and are raised in thousands every year by market gardeners and others, are allowed to remain in the seed-bed eighteen months, and are kept clean and free from weeds, when they will readily sell at from 4s to nearly 10s per 100 to farmers and others, who grow for their own supply or for sale . . .

No return of importance can be expected for nearly six years . . .

The young trees should be transplanted into well-prepared ground 3 feet apart where they remain two years and then they are fit for grafting.

In February they are headed, or cut off at about 8 or 9 inches of the ground; at the same time scions or grafts of approved kinds are taken off and their ends laid in the ground until grafting time, which is in March or early in April.'

There is little written history of the development of West Country cider apples. It is generally accepted that outside of the Great Houses where making excellent cider was always taken as seriously as wine making in Europe, little cider apple selection was done with any purpose. There was reputed to be stiff competition between the more wealthy landowners for recognition of the quality of the cider made from their own orchards. They would certainly have known others who might have been prepared to compare notes and perhaps swap both cider and a few graft cuttings from promising trees, without giving away too many of the secrets of their success. Their interest must have been intense since there are many books on orchards and preparation of cider dating from before the 18th century and throughout the 19th, most of them valuable then as now, that would only have been available to a minority of wealthy people . The publication of Hogg's prodigious *Herefordshire Pomona* of 1878 [only 600 copies ever printed], for the Woolhope Naturalists' Field Club with all its illustrations of the revered fruits of the time, is testimony to the seriousness with which the subject was taken.

A few Somerset nurseries in the 19th century, such as Porters of Lambrook, propagated cider apples in addition to their main lines of eating and cooking apples, for example Porters Perfection and Lambrook Pippin. Scott's nursery not far away in Merriott certainly listed many apple varieties and introduced some local selections like Lopen Neverblight, sadly no longer extant. Their 1873 catalogue also listed Siberian Bittersweet, a progeny of Thomas Andrew Knight, famed horticulturalist and early president of the RHS. The well known Yarlington Mill was listed and sold most profitably by Harry Masters' nursery in the late 19th century, together with his own Jersey and other local seedlings with the desirable local bittersweet flavour. The 1826 catalogue of Sweets and Miller, nurserymen of Bristol, listed many rare old cider apple names along with the popular garden apples of the time. A few of them still exist, but there is no evidence that they produced any of their own new selections.

ROOTSTOCKS, STEM-BUILDERS AND WARNINGS

Up until the middle of the last century it would have been customary to graft the chosen variety onto a seedling stock. Formerly this would have been a free stock, a seedling grown from random seed collection usually from pomace waste after fruit pressing. This method gave somewhat unpredictable results since the influence of seedlings would vary from tree to tree. By the early 20th century vegetatively propagated selected crabs were often used, the most popular being Malling Crab C, a useful semi-dwarfing stock that would give a predictable tree size and vigour.

Later still, seedlings from Yarlington Mill or Tremletts Bitter were often used as stocks since they could be relied upon to come fairly true to type and their influence on the variety would be fairly uniform.

More recently vegetatively grown, semi-dwarfing stocks have been used for bush trees, the most popular being MM106, MM111, M26 and M25. The size and vigour of trees grown on these is very predictable.. MM106 is the most commonly used since it is moderately dwarfing and produces an easily manageable tree from 4-6 m, depending of the variety, however it is fairly susceptible to crown rot [caused by the fungus *Phytophthora* in poorly drained land] so it is not suitable for sites subject to periodic water-logging or winter wet. M26, is also semi-dwarfing and produces a smaller tree than MM106 with less vigour, but which is inclined to crop most precociously. This rootstock is not suitable for weak varieties like Dabinett and it requires the trees to be supported with a stake for a longer time. MM111 is a vigorous stock, producing a larger tree than MM106. It is tolerant of drought and suitable for difficult or windy sites, areas that may be periodically wet, or land where the soil depth may be restricted. M25 is the most vigorous stock . It has a deep, strong root system and is especially suitable for standard trees giving excellent support. It produces the largest, most robust trees for difficult conditions.

Traditionally standard trees would have had a stem-builder, a bud of a strong, quick growing variety grafted onto the main rootstock. Being a vigorous triploid variety, Morgan Sweet has been widely used as a stem builder for standard trees of other varieties since the early part of the 20th century. Usually it would have been headworked when it was well established with a framework of about ten branches onto each of which a single stick of the chosen variety would be grafted.

Bulmers Norman, Morgan Sweet, Court Royal [Sweet Blenheim] and Lambrook Pippin have all been locally favoured by various nurseries. Bulmers Norman is by far the most common to the present day since it will successfully produce a stout trunk in two years. But it is vigorous and frequently proves too strong for the chosen scion variety as the tree ages. Eventually the Bulmers Norman branches below the union take over the head of the tree and yellow apples amongst the red give the game away. The secret is to prune out all stembuilder shoots below the graft as the trees are trained and pull off the suckers from the stock before they overcome the head.

So care is needed when selecting fruit from an old tree for identification. First check that there is a stem-builder by finding the union where it joins the rootstock. Then seek out the graft union at around two metres up, where the variety joins the stem. Make sure that the fruit is coming from branches above the graft. Trace the branches upward to check their ID before collecting wood for budding and grafting and avoid the risk of propagating only Bulmers Norman trees! Some trees may not have a stem-builder, but will have been top-worked onto a strong rootstock that has been grown up to provide a trunk. More recently, some nurseries have produced standard trees grown up from bush tree maidens. Their size and strength as a standard tree will usually be compromised, lacking the advantage of a stem-builder.

Beware of the scoundrel with the budding knife! It is an easy exercise to top-work a tree if the original variety doesn't suit. There may well be more than one variety as well as the original and the stem. The legendary Punch Garland had a sense of humour. He was well known for putting rogue grafts of odd varieties into the head of trees when the owners weren't looking.

ACQUIRING YOUR OWN TREES

There are several good nurseries at present who produce cider apple trees of excellent quality. It may be possible to buy just what you want 'off the shelf' from their lists. If there is something special that you desire, something not listed but out of the ordinary, then that will have to be propagated specially to order. Normally this process will take 2 years to a bush tree, sometimes longer for a standard tree of your choice, so give the order to the nursery plenty of time.

There are two ways to do your own propagation. The easiest is by grafting. You will need a suitable rootstock. These can either be grown from seed or more easily and quicker, be acquired from a nursery and grown on to a reasonable size at home. Alternatively, a small tree of an unwanted variety could be used. Grafting is a relatively easy technique, bearing in mind one or two rules; cut the wood of your variety when it is leafless and dormant, keep it cool, prevent it drying out, then wait until the stock begins growth in the following spring, in April before you insert your grafts. You should expect to get your new variety growing quickly in the first season. Budding is a little more fiddly to do but success comes with practice. This procedure takes a little longer to get your result, but it is a job to be done in the warmer weather during July and August.

A HEALTH WARNING!

Some varieties with the most desirable vintage qualities come with the most displeasing faults. Kingston Black, renowned for its excellent balanced bittersharp juice and capable of making the most excellent single varietal cider on occasion, has many faults. It suffers from brown rot, scab, and canker. It is too vigorous, tardy to come into cropping and then may only fruit well every other year. Its flowers are small and squinny, almost stemless and shunned by bees. Stoke Red has even better bittersharp qualities, but it crops biennially, its fruit is small and late, and the trees resemble an unmanageable willow bush. Porters Perfection, another bittersharp is so late in maturing it often gets left to lie on the ground. These varieties are really for the enthusiastic connoisseur.

When choosing your varieties it is worth bearing in mind that although they may make excellent cider, many of them will come with a health warning!

MOSAICS AND LATENTS

It is worth taking another warning when collecting propagation material from very old trees. Even if they are growing strongly and healthily, it is an almost certainty that they will have become infected with a virus or two over the years, transmitted either through pruning knives or some insect vector. Some apple viruses have alarming symptoms. Mosaic virus shows as a bright yellow checkerboard pattern on the odd leaf but fortunately this virus is not very debilitating. The more sinister *latent* viruses, may not show symptoms at all but can seriously weaken a tree and cause its power and cropping to decline.

Much work was done on fruit tree viruses at Long Ashton in the latter half of 20th century. A successful virus elimination, heat treatment and re-testing project resulted in a list of cleaned up cider varieties many of which are now still available from reputable tree nurseries and it is recommended that these should be used whenever possible. It has to be said though that a young tree taken as a graft from an old infected tree will often be healthier than its parent, since some of the virus's influence can be overcome in the process.

The National Fruit and Cider Institute at Long Ashton

A BRIEF HISTORY

In the late 19th century, C W Radcliffe-Cooke, MP for Hereford, sometimes called the 'MP for cider', commented on the sad state of the cider industry *'Ciders and perries are all alike and only to be told from vinegar by a highly discriminating palate'.*

It was an opinion shared by many, since around this time there were a few commercial cider factories making and bottling indifferent cider for sale to the general public. Every West Country farm still made cider from its orchards well into the 20th century and was expected to provide it free to those working on the farm, especially during the thirsty work of harvest and sheep shearing, although, after the Truck Act farm cider could no longer legally be accepted as part of the farm labourer's wages.

However, the significance Radcliffe-Cookes's caustic words resonated with the thoughts of many influential people in the South West, not least Robert Neville-Grenville of Butleigh Court near Glastonbury. He was well known for his appreciation of fine cider and also his extensive collection of apple trees, many of them collected from France. A member of the Bath & West Council, he was concerned about the lack of underlying knowledge of the principles of cider making and the crudeness of the methods used in cider production on the farms. In 1893 he employed the services of Frederick Lloyd, a cheese microbiologist and analyst from London, to begin a series of experiments to improve the fermentation process. Such was the success of his trial work, that Neville-Grenville was able to persuade other members of the Bath and West Council from all the cider growing counties of the West; Brecon, Cornwall, Devon, Dorset, Gloucester, Hereford, Monmouth, Somerset and Worcester, that full time effort in a permanent place should be instituted for the advancement of the knowledge and skills of cidermaking. Thus with the aid of some grants from both the Royal Bath and West Society and the Board of Agriculture, the National Fruit and Cider Institute was born in 1903 at Long Ashton and Frederick Lloyd began to put some science into cider making.

Professor BPT Barker was duly appointed Director and farmers and orchard owners were invited to submit samples of their fruit for assessment and for trial cider making. Data recorded in those early Long Ashton Reports was of the typical juice qualities, specific gravity [SG], acidity [as % malic acid content] and tannin [as % total tannins]. The juice of single varieties was fermented under strict control and many notes were made of the rate and conditions of the fermentation. Once the work became widely recognized as an annual practice, the owners of the fruit samples were invited back to taste the results in an ongoing and eagerly anticipated series of the celebrated Tasting Days. Although these were generally regarded as entertaining social occasions, the competitiveness between the participants and the kudos of an award for excellence, served as a first-rate method of education and initiation into the intricacies of good cider making. Thus the reputation of West Country cider was once more restored.

It was Professor Barker who set the formal classification standards for juice and cider assessment; bittersweets as those apples with a tannin content of more than 0.20% but with an acidity of less than 0.45%, sharps as those with little tannin but more than 0.45% acid, bittersharps with a combination of both tannin over 0.20% and acidity over 0.45%, and pure sweets, those with little tannin or acidity.

LONG ASHTON TRIAL ORCHARDS

By 1912, the Institute had become the Department of Agricultural and Horticultural Research for the University of Bristol. Soon the research extended to orchard trials of those varieties that showed promise. Orchards of standard trees, very often on seedling stocks, were planted at Long Ashton and members and farmers were invited to grow selected varieties on their own farms.

By 1934 the Institute had amassed enough information from their experiments in both the laboratory and in the trial orchards to be able to make recommendations for suitable plantings. Now classed as Vintage Varieties, Prof Barker's list of recommendations named over 80 varieties, their flowering and harvesting times and their cidermaking qualities. A further round of trial orchard planting was undertaken with these. However, in time, many of them proved impractical to grow or revealed disorders of some sort and by 1949 his list was refined to include only those that had performed well in the trial orchards. He added a list of regional choices, those varieties most suitable for growing in Devon, Somerset and Hereford and Gloucester. Such was the respect for his judgement and that of his expert staff at Long Ashton, that many growers followed his recommendations and planted their orchards accordingly.

Prof. Barker's List Of Recommended Vintage Cider Apple Varieties 1949

Sweet:
Court Royal
Sweet Alford
Sweet Coppin

Sharp:
Backwell Red
Crimson King

Bittersweet:
Bulmer's Norman
Dabinett
Tardive Forestier

Ashton Brown Jersey
Tremlett's Bitter
Yarlington Mill

Bittersharp:
Stoke Red
Improved Foxwhelp
Kingston Black

Prof Barker's regional choice for Somerset included Morgan Sweet, Red Jersey, Dove and Hangdown, all little grown nowadays with the exception of Morgan Sweet. His Devon selection included Ellis Bitter, Kingston Bitter, Colman's Seedling and Langworthy, and for Hereford & Gloucester he chose Michelin, White Norman, Frederick and several French varieties.

The preferred list of recommendations was further narrowed so that by the time that the last standard trial orchards were planted in the early 1950s, the choice was reduced to around a dozen varieties, such as Tremletts Bitter, Medaille d'Or, Ashton Brown Jersey, Yarlington Mill, Sweet Coppin and Sweet Alford.

FIRST GENERATION BUSH CIDER ORCHARDS

During the 1950s and '60s a few experimental bush orchard trials were made using reliable varieties on dwarfing stocks, but it was not until the 1970s that bush trees were planted in any numbers. Thanks largely to a sustained television advertising campaign, cider had become extremely popular and more fruit was needed to meet the demand for raw material for bottled and draft cider on a scale never before experienced. Rapid decisions were made on the choice of variety and those that had performed well in the old orchards as standard trees were chosen for the new bush orchards. Many hundreds of acres were planted in Hereford for Bulmers and in Somerset and Dorset for Taunton Cider and Showerings. Both Bulmers and Taunton Cider encouraged independent growers to plant orchards on contract to supply fruit annually to their factories. Showerings had a number of their own managed farms as did Bulmers. The varieties grown were predominantly Michelin, Dabinett, Yarlington Mill, Harry Masters Jersey, Chisel Jersey, Somerset Redstreak, Tremletts Bitter, Taylors Sweet, Bulmers Norman and Browns Apple. Brown Snout and Vilberie were fairly popular as late flowering varieties and Reinne des Hatives and Nehou were occasionally planted to provide early season fruit. Taunton Cider's nursery manager favoured the newly named local varieties, Stembridge Clusters, Stembridge Jersey and Coat Jersey for Somerset orchards. Occasionally less well known varieties such as Fillbarrel, Improved Lambrook Pippin, Breakwells Seedling, Porters Perfection and Stoke Red were included. These first bush orchards were planted with different varieties in adjacent rows to aid pollination or with the pollinators as single trees to every five or six of the main variety. This pattern was to prove difficult to manage when spraying or harvesting the fruit .

THE SECOND GENERATION OF BUSH CIDER ORCHARDS

By the early 1980s it was becoming clear that some cider varieties were far superior in terms of production and, since less value was put on the cider making vintage qualities of the fruit, the most regular cropping and productive varieties were favoured in their stead as more contracts were made and more and more trees were planted. These new orchards tended to be planted in blocks of single varieties, perhaps five rows, sometimes considerably larger areas, with similar adjacent blocks of other varieties that should flower at the same time. Probably the first single variety Kingston Black bush orchard was planted at Sheppy's Cider in 1980.

By far the greatest area , nearly 50%, was planted up to the two varieties, Michelin and Dabinett and some of the early, difficult and biennially performing varieties like Tremletts Bitter and Nehou were grubbed. This preponderance of mid season fruit led to big logistical problems in the cider factories as vast quantities of fruit arrived at the mills in the same short few weeks of October. Long Ashton was asked to come up with some new or unusual varieties that could be relied on to mature in late September or early October. A search was made and several regional and foreign earlies were put on trial but none were without their own problems. Of these the best are Ellis Bitter, Major and White Jersey but Ashton Bitter, a great hope at the time, proved too unreliably biennial and many new orchards were either grubbed or worked over with a new variety.

THE THIRD GENERATION, THE 21st CENTURY CIDER APPLES

This lack of suitable early maturing varieties led to the decision to start a breeding program at Long Ashton with the aim of producing a range of new cultivars with all the desirable criteria; regular cropping, early maturing, large fruited, easy to manage and [relatively] disease free. Thus crosses were made in 1985 between the popular Dabinett and Michelin and the early juice variety James Grieve and the aromatic bright red Worcester Pearmain. Many years later the Girls emerged, a selection of 29 new cultivars, most mild bittersweet, some bittersharp and some with good juice character, a range suitable for planting for many purposes and under different conditions.

Over 2,600 acres, 791,100 trees of these new selections were planted in the years between 2006 and 2013 [the time of writing, 2013] The most popular of these are Amanda, Angela, Debbie, Fiona, Gilly, Hastings, Helen's Apple, Jane, Lizzy, Prince William, Three Counties and Vicky. A further 375,000 trees are destined to be planted in the next three or four years, and such are their qualities and relative ease of management, that a long spell of popularity is anticipated.

Re-Discovering Cider Apples

DECLINE, FALL AND REVIVAL

There are usually plenty of apples of one sort or another going begging every autumn; garden surpluses, the odd trees in field corners and hedges, but most of these will not have much character and quality to lend to your cider. It is well worth sorting out the real thing. You success will depend on some good detective work.

Although traditional orchards in the South West have steadily declined since the late 19th century, they were a significant feature of the countryside up until the 2nd World War. Most farmers considered them an asset, but changes in agriculture brought about by the war put pressure on the land to be used more profitably for crops to feed the nation. Many small scale cidermakers were unable to survive the 1930s recession. A similar fate befell many of the smaller breweries who were bought up and merged into large scale commercial businesses. Cider drinking became less popular and beer took its share. The final nails were put in the coffin by the 'grubbing grants' from the 1960s that provided further incentive for orchards to be replaced with more lucrative crops.

All this had a devastating effect on the survival of our traditional cider orchards and the landscape was irrevocably changed. In 1883 Devon had the second largest acreage of orchards next to Herefordshire, but it had lost nearly 85% of them through agricultural conversion, mainly arable crops, by 1989. A story repeated in Dorset and to a lesser extent in Somerset. The cessation of the grubbing grants did slow but not stop the decline. The trend has been slowly reversed thanks largely to the hard work by Common Ground in promoting awareness of the value and traditions of our countryside, its environment and local landscape. Several County Councils have given financial support to replacing and renovating old orchards with local varieties of apples. And thankfully, cider drinking has seen a grand revival over the last decade, bringing with it a great demand for the raw material.

But in some places it is still possible to find the remnants of those old orchards that survived the impoverishment, perhaps only as a few trees, even single trees in back gardens where orchards once were. These finds are like gold dust and well worth looking for since the chances are they will be some of the best cider apple varieties.

HOT SPOTS

Although cider orchards are fairly widespread in the West and even the odd trees can commonly be found tucked away in unlikely places, there are several regions where fruit trees thrive most successfully. Better topography, better soils, greater traditions and equitable climate combine to give rise to hot spots of surviving old trees and more modern orcharding. Although much of Somerset and Hereford have long been clothed with cider trees, the heart of West Country orcharding is really in the excellent lands of central Somerset; Martock, Kingsbury Episcopi, Stembridge and away towards Wincanton. The rich alluvial soils of the Exe valley are another focus providing suitable sites that once made orcharding a commercial proposition to supply the plentiful local cider factories. Further west there are many steep slopes in the mellow rain-shadow climate of the Tamar valley and in the sheltered, less accessible villages of south Devon where orchards once supplied more local needs. But West Dorset is different again. It is an 'island' on its own riven with wooded combes and lofty ridgeways. Here will still be many an undiscovered secret. Good hunting!

SEARCHING FOR DORSET'S LOST ORCHARDS

In 1938, P T H Pickford, Cider Orcharding Advisor to the National Fruit and Cider Institute [Long Ashton Research Station] wrote in an article;

'According to many farmers, Dorset was the first county in England to make cider. It is claimed that the art of cider-making was first introduced

into this county by monks from northern France who settled in a village near Bridport some time before the Norman Conquest . . . Whether this be true or not, Dorset certainly ranks with the counties in the West of England which have produced cider for centuries.'

His notes give us a clear picture of the extent of Dorset cider orchards in 1938, and also provide us with vital clues towards rediscovering those that survive to this day.

'Although the acreage of Dorset's orcharding is small compared with that of the other counties, it must be remembered that apart from the comparative size of Dorset, the soil in a big proportion of the county is of the type totally unsuitable for fruit culture. In those areas where the soil is suitable however the orchards thrive and are numerously planted and here the production of cider fruit is as much a business as it is in Somerset and Devon.

*'The largest cider orchard area lies in West Dorset towards the Devon border including and around the neighbourhood of **Loders, Powerstock, Netherbury, Beaminster, Broadwindsor** and **Stoke Abbott**. There are smaller areas around **Thorncombe, Whitchurch, Wootton Fitzpaine, Chideock** and **Symondsbury**. Most of these orchards are planted in medium loams derived from the middle lias, but there are also quite a number planted in the very light soil of the Bridport sands, in particular around **Melplash**.*

*'In other parts of Dorset the orchard areas are smaller and widely scattered throughout the county. There is a considerable acreage around **Leigh** and **Chetnole** where a good proportion are planted in heavy loams from the Oxford clay. Scattered orchards are found around both **Gillingham** and **Shaftsbury** and again around **Sturminster Newton**, but cider orchards are more numerous in the neighbourhood of **Child Okeford, Shillingstone** and **Hammoor** where a good deal of cider is produced. Yet another area worthy of mention is that around **Piddlehinton** and **Piddletrenthide** where numerous orchards are found growing in the alluvium of the narrow valleys.'*

Certainly in Thomas Hardy's time there were plenty of orchards in the Blackmore Vale. He even makes the distinction between good bittersweets and John apples, presumably those for the kitchen [*The Woodlanders* and Giles Winterborne, a man who grew them]. Sadly, because of this and in spite of Pickford's professional instruction, cider-making never seems to have re-gained a secure status in Dorset, but has remained an extremely local pursuit. Orchards that once supplied the liquid requirements of many staff and farm workers have now declined to skeletal echo of their pre-War status. Unlike the other cider counties, Dorset has never had any major cider producing factories such as Whiteways or Showerings, rather breweries predominate. Perhaps now with the resurgence of interest in craft cider making in Dorset, cider orchards will once again be part of the permanent landscape.

THE DATA PROJECT

Nick Poole, a Dorset man who had founded both the West Milton Cider Club and the legendary Powerstock Annual Cider Festival, was keen to find out just what true Dorset cider apples and their cider tasted like so that he could continue the good work of making authentic tasting craft cider. To maintain regional distinctiveness, local varieties would be the best choice but these needed to be identified and their locations mapped. With much local support, Nick and I were able to secure a grant from Leader Plus/Chalk and Cheese to start our project which he dubbed the DATA Project [Dorset Apple Tree Analysis]. Work began to locate possible sources of trees but aside of Pickford's notes, written records of Dorset varieties and their locations are scarce.

A search in Dorchester's Heritage Centre of OS maps made around 1903 showed nearly every village surrounded by a ring of orchards. We talked to people who once worked on the land, those who made and drank cider. What they reported confirmed that many village orchards had seen their last days in the 1960s when grants were offered to clear the land. Just a few useful cookers or eating apples were often the only survivors. The clearances later made way for new buildings, village infill and sadly, the proliferation of road names like 'Orchard Close' and 'Old Orchard Way'. Just tombstones where orchards once stood.

Response from articles about our project in several local papers gave us plenty of leads to follow which took us all over the county and to quite an amazing array of trees. Some were located in large well tended orchards that were still in full production, but always the names of varieties had been lost. Others we literally had to fight our way through bushes and hedges to find often very dishevelled, lonely old trees that time and man had forgotten. Much detective work was then needed to link names to varieties we found and to re-name unknown varieties with potential for cider-making.

To assess the juice and cider-making qualities of each variety found, we sent a juice sample to the Thatchers Cider Company's laboratory for detailed laboratory analysis. Our exploratory taste-testing of the fruit had already told us that in

West Dorset they were predominantly sharp or bitter-sharp in flavour and sometimes dual purpose. Laboratory analysis confirmed our initial deductions. We concluded that the local preference for cider in West Dorset was much like that over the border in Devon, rather low in tannin and quite sharp to the taste. As we went further north and to central Dorset, we found that in this part of the world the cidermakers knew the value of tannin, for full bittersweets and good bittersharps predominate. Here close to the border with Somerset, an historically wandering border, the local taste was for a well rounded, astringent cider. Something that lingered on the palate and invited a further draught.

The 21st century resurgence of interest in small scale cider making in the county desperately needs vintage quality fruit for making good quality products rather than the indifferent tasting cookers from poorly nourished trees that so often get used. Clearly there are many unique local Dorset cider apple varieties worth keeping, but trees we found were ageing and in need of care and replacement. We did the best we could to collect suitable clean propagating material for disease free young trees. These have been distributed widely to small orchards and enthusiasts. Also there are three full collections of our findings at Thatchers Cider Orchards, Sandford, Somerset, and in Dorset at Linden Lea Orchard, Melplash and Liberty Farm, Closworth. Hopefully all will be looked after, cherished and added to over the years as more Dorset cider apples come to be discovered.

TITHE MAPS, OS AND GOOGLE

Tithe records were compiled in the early 19th century to record and appropriately tax land in every parish. The acreage, ownership and predominant use; agricultural, orchard, cottage garden, common, were all recorded. They usually give the field and orchard names, farm by farm, and tell you who owned the land, who was renting it, what it was used for and the tithe. Tithe maps accompany the written records were orchards are depicted by hand-drawn fruit trees, easy to see. The maps are usually publicly available in county heritage centres. Some have been digitalised and may be available on line. A visit to your county archives will prove fascinating and provide an insight into the village activities and way of life nearly a hundred and seventy five years ago.

In the 1890s the Ordnance Survey published very accurate six inch maps, so orchards of that time were plotted with certainty. These too should be available for public scrutiny, as will the later OS maps dating from 1900. Sadly further updated versions of OS maps display less and less in the way of orchards and

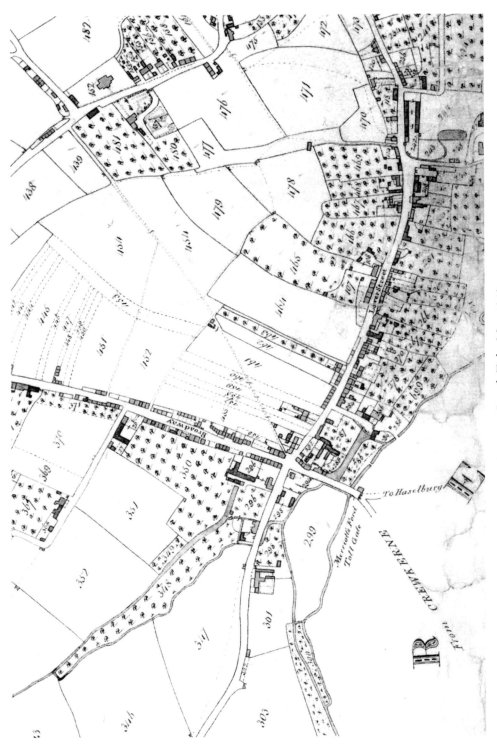

Merriott Parish Tithe Map 1843

more of the expansion of the small villages out into the surrounding farm land as housing to accommodate the increasing rural population.

Nevertheless, it is a useful exercise to compare a modern OS map and the original tithe map of your area. This will give you an idea of where the orchards once were and you will be able to check on the current land use to see if it is at all possible that the remnants of orchards, even the odd tree, might still exist. Areas of 'wasteland' in industrial areas, back gardens and parks are all good spots to try.

The corner of the four foot square 1843 tithe map of Merriott, my local village, illustrated here shows broad areas of orchards surrounding the cottages and their back gardens. Many orchards were shown still in apparent good health on the 1884–87 OS maps of the village and even the 1900 version. But now a hundred years later there are few signs of their presence, most trees have disappeared and the land is down to grazing, extended gardens or more houses. Happily there is one significant survivor on the glebe land near the church [top right hand corner of the map] where a handful of trees yield apples most years. Some may be the originals mapped a hundred and sixty years ago, but they are more likely to be replacements that were planted to fill in the gaps as the originals aged and died. I am convinced that a concentrated search of back gardens in the village would unearth a few more gems and one day I shall have to do it.

Google Maps can prove very useful in your searches since you can zoom in to likely spots and examine any trees with moderate clarity. Well kept and relatively modern orchards are distinguished by their close planting and uniformity. You should be able to distinguish between standard trees that appear as discrete blobs in a cross-hatch pattern, older traditional orchards with bigger trees with gaps between where trees have died, and bush orchards which show as continuous hedgerows.

Having listed your 'possibles', the next move is to walk, map in hand in the search for trees. Check with land owners before scaling fences and straying onto private land. Most people are curious to hear that their trees might be interesting enough to be of value. Take the opportunity of talking to local inhabitants who just might know of the odd tree, a well known local apple variety or perhaps the history and whereabouts of an old orchard or cider mill. Many older people in villages are often very knowledgeable. Having been brought up in their village their childhood memories will often recall picking apples and making cider. This essential information can often be more useful in locating old orchard sites than any maps.

Left: *Part of Merriott Tithe Map [Ref D\D/Rt/M/413].*
Reproduced by permission from Somerset Archives and Local Studies Service.

Names, Synonyms and Mistakes

Many names are clearly descriptive; Hangdown with its weeping tree habit, Silver Cup with its broad, deep eye basin, Sheep's Nose, there are many shaped like this, Bell and Lady's Finger, longer than it is broad. Bishop's Nose is intriguing. Perhaps it was long and red, but it is sadly lost without a description. Although he disappeared in 1895, the Bishop must have had a sharp tongue; his juice was recorded in the Bath and West list as very acid!

Many bear the name to carry the fame of the originator like Tremlett's Bitter, Ellis Bitter, Dabinett [although sounding French, this is very much a local Somerset name], Dunkerton's Late, Brown's Apple and Harry Masters' Jersey. Porter's Perfection which records the success of nurseryman, Charles Porter of Lambrook, certainly is an excellent bittersharp. Many are named after the village or place where they came from; Kingston Black [reputedly Kingston St Mary, near Taunton], Lambrook Pippin, Stoke Red [after Rodney Stoke], Gatcombe [Gatcombe Farm near Long Ashton], Yarlington Mill, and many others. Ashton Brown Jersey and Ashton Bitter were named in honour of the Research Station.

Other names are more romantic such as the pale and blushing Fair Maid of Taunton, also called Moonshines. Being blond, she shows up well in the dark and harvesting can go on after work in the short autumn days. Hoary Morning has a waxy bloom on its cheeks like a coating of frost, but is also mischievously called Bachelor's Glory! Tom Putt sometimes has a strange bluish, meaty bloom which may account for its synonym, Marrowbone. Sops in Wine is a very old apple with a name that suits its dark red flesh blotched with milk. It is easy to see how Ten Commandments gets its name. When the apple is cut in half, there are ten red dots around the core, from the ten red veins running through the white flesh.

Unfortunately, Fillbarrel's name is less appropriate. It has a reputation for being very biennial and so fills the barrels only every other year. Poor Man's Profit is wistful but perhaps optimistic. Never-Deceive-Me or Seek-No-Further are names of integrity and Truckle and Buskin conjure a pleasant rustic picture. Alas, many of these apples are lost from memory now.

There was at one time a 'fake' Slack-ma-Girdle widely distributed in the Totnes to Staverton district. It was almost indistinguishable from the true Slack except that the foliage was paler, the fruit dryer and, worst of all, the trees tended to split right down the trunk when about forty years old and heavily in crop. This was known locally as 'Splitter'.

Some names describe the properties of the juice. Tom Tanners was reputed to be devastatingly astringent and used only sparingly. Other names suggest outstanding vintage qualities such as Gin or Port Wine, and Porter's Perfection still has a reputation for producing an excellent cider. Some names extol other virtues of the cider made from them, particularly the effect on the human digestive system. Runaway, Slack-ma-Girdle, Burstout and Little Trotts leave little to the imagination.

In the early part of the 20th century, when the Cider Institute advertised for one-and-all to submit their favourite cider apples for judging, there was much competition for the kudos of the annual cidermaking prizes. Many of the apples must have been seedlings, often hastily named before sending in, and often bearing the name of the sender in the hope of fame, like Jenning's Seedling. Some may have been sent in with incorrect names which later proved to be distinct varieties, leading to much confusion and perpetuation of mistakes. Synonyms often arose through the need to invent a name for one lost or forgotten. Sometimes known varieties were high-jacked and given a false name for the sake of finding a 'new variety' with guaranteed merit. Incorrect synonyms also arose through spelling mistakes, or from copying down names phonetically, especially when delivered in a broad Somerset accent. During the first half of the last century, most of these discrepancies were sorted out and varieties with any vintage promise were collected and grown at Long Ashton or in Trial Orchards around the counties under their confirmed name.

Some cider apples bear a 'Royal' name, such as Court Royal, Royal Jersey and Royal Wildling. There could be two reasons for this. It may simply be that the cider prepared from them was considered so exceptional that it was fit for royalty. But in these 'Royal' apples, the eye of sepals is curiously erect and resembles a tiny pointed crown. A fanciful mark of superiority perhaps.

Then there is Buttery Door, a variety that bears many synonyms. Mr Warren, cidermaker of Netherbury, Dorset and expert on local orchards and fruit, sent a sample with that name to the Cider Institute in 1927. But I rather fancy the alternative name Buttery Dough, evoking the aroma of fresh baked apple pie. It was displayed at the RHS Exhibition in 1934, as a cooking apple from Devon and as a cider apple from Dorset, both under the name Buttery d'Or. This French sounding identity is perhaps a little too exotic for such an unassuming variety. Clearly a very old apple, it is possible that *Buttery D'Or* may be a the remnants of a very old name. In Old English, *bud leah* or *buttleigh* meant a cultivated meadow, and *dor* was a gate. I like to think that the original tree could have been *'the tree by the gate in the meadow – Buttleigh Dor'*. Possible?

JERSEYS

There has always been much discussion about the origins of the group of bittersweet apples known as 'jerseys'. These are of Somerset origin and were sometimes referred to as 'georges', named after a brown earthenware vessel used for carrying cider in the past. There was once speculation that 'jersey' was a corruption of the word 'jaisy', meaning bitter in Somerset dialect, but this has never been substantiated. Although it was once thought that these apples originally came from the island of Jersey, it is most unlikely. There are many traditional Jersey bittersweets, some similar to their Breton counterparts, but none is the same as any of our 'jerseys'. Since there was once busy trading of fruit from the Channel Isles for cidermaking in times of shortage on the mainland, Jersey bittersweet apples must have gained a good reputation. Perhaps the taste, now so characteristic to Somerset cider, was reacquired in those days. So our 'jerseys' may have come to us indirectly from the Channel Isles. It is reasonable to imagine that they began as seedlings grown from the pomace waste thrown out after pressing imported fruit, and were brought up as natives. Certainly in the latter part of the 19th century, many French bittersweet varieties were introduced with the intention of improving the standards of our cider. None of these are called 'jerseys', nor are they much like our 'jerseys' either. Although, more common in the West Midlands, they do crop up in some of the old Somerset orchards that were planted in the 20th century. Those that do not have French names are recognised as 'Normans', such as Bulmer's, White, Cherry, Sherrington Norman and many others. Now, in the 21st century, Somerset has a fine collection of 'jerseys'; Chisel Jersey, Broadleaf, Coat, Red and Royal, Stable and Stembridge Jerseys, White Jersey and Harry Masters' Jersey and more.

CHANGES FOR THE BETTER?

Then there are the 'Improved' apples but this claim often needs to be taken with a pinch of salt. If a cider variety had a fault, its fruit was too small, it was prone to disease or poor crops, there were often attempts to re-propagate from its own seed in the hope of improving on the original. A rash of 'new varieties' was created at the height of the Cider Institute activity during the early part of the 20th century. Dove is one that was tinkered with leading to Stone Dove, Dove Seedling and others. Improved Dove did have some real improvements, its fruit is much bigger and less scabby, but the experiment was not always successful. Although very easy growing and healthy, Improved Kingston Black has greatly inferior vintage qualities to its forbear being just plain sharp with little tannin. Improved Hangdown is just as weak and weeping as its parent, and the new Lambrook Pippin, like Improved Kingston Black, lost much of its tannin. Improved Woodbine could even be said to be inferior to the original.

NAMES FOR RE-DISCOVERED DORSET APPLES

Where identifiable, the DATA Project was able to put the correct name to many apple trees that were discovered, but some defied the most in-depth detective work. No trace could be found of their identities in any reference book, list or apple tree collection. When these varieties were propagated for circulation, we took the liberty of giving them new names as follows:

Dashayes Crab, Golly Knapp, Hains Late Sweet, Loders, Marlpits Late, Marnhull Bitters, Marnhull Mill, Meadow Cottage and Tangy.

Should the true identities ever come to light we would be delighted to amend things.

Putting a Name To Your Fruit

The development of a discriminating palate is a prerequisite for the orchard detective, because the first and most important move towards identifying a cider apple is to taste it. They can all be loosely grouped into any one of the four taste categories as bittersweets or pure sweets, bittersharps or sharps, so it essential to be able to detect the presence of tannin by its bitterness or astringency. Initially some people find it quite difficult to distinguish between bitter and acid tastes, but once the tangy citric taste of a pure sharp cider apple has been experienced, it is easy to separate the encounter from the warmer, furry, tea taste of a good bittersweet. Both are a surprise to the novice palate but once acquired, the tastes are unexpectedly addictive. With practice it soon becomes possible to differentiate between a mouth-drawing sensation of astringency and a more tongue-furring bitter taste. Soon it will also be clear why a true sharp apple has a more valuable flavour for cider-making than a culinary tasting dual purpose apple.

Season

Cider apples usually flower two or more weeks after other apples. They also tend to mature, ready for juicing much later Although the time when the fruit is ready for harvesting varies greatly from year to year, there are three broad maturity seasons for cider apples; *Early*, from the end of September until early October; *Mid season*, ready sometime in October; and *Late*, not ready until November. Season is a strong character. Even if an apple specimen fits a visual description but it is mature at the wrong time – your ID is most probably incorrect.

The GISS

The next move is to study the least variable visual characters and the most stable are the overall shape and the stem. Birdwatchers often go by the GISS, the general impression of size and shape of their example and with practice, this works with identifying apple varieties. Each variety in the following list is described briefly first using its most noticeable characters.

To make an accurate identification, it is essential to collect a good, fresh, representative sample of your fruit, not less than 20 fruits if possible, preferably sampled randomly when they are ripe and falling freely. Stored apples are almost impossible to identify, since apples like people, all begin to look the same when they become tired and old.

Beware – the half fruit drawings are only intended to show the characteristic shape of each variety and do not give a true indication of relative size.

Shape

Cider apples fall into several basic shapes as shown in the picture. Some typical examples are: *Round*; Stoke Red, Ashton Bitter: *Oblate*; Vallis Apple, Improved Kingston Black: *Cylindrical*; Dunkerton's Late, Sweet Coppin: *Conical*; this includes most of the 'jerseys': *Flattened conical*; Pennard Bitter, Chisel Jersey: *Elongated conical*; Bell, Pig's Nose and Long Tom. Many varieties may lie somewhere in between, such as Cap of Liberty which is between conical and cylindrical.

But beware, usually the king fruits, the first fruits to set in the cluster, are a different shape from the later fruits. Kingston Black often has many of both. The king fruits are cylindrical and the rest are flattened conical, appearing almost like two different varieties.

The shape of the base is an important character. A wide base such as found in Yarlington Mill is a constant feature in this variety. Many bittersweet jerseys are 'snouted' or 'waisted' with a distinct constricted nose. Fused fruits are sometimes found on several varieties but are frequent in Porter's Perfection.

The shape and size of fruit from a young tree can be unreliable and misleading. Best to wait till the first good crop.

Stem and Stem Basin

The stem length varies only slightly within a variety and is a good diagnostic feature. Examine all your sample of fruit and come to a majority decision.; stem absent, within the cavity, projecting slightly, projecting distinctly or projecting considerably.

The stem basin has to be judged in relation to the overall size of the fruit, thus similar dimensions may be called small in large fruits but large in small ones. An irregular stem basin, flattened on one side, occurs in Backwell Red.

Eye basin and calyx

Like the stem basin, the size of the eye basin needs to be judged in relation to the size of the fruit. Some apples are characteristically ribbed or angular in section, with ribs sometimes starting at the eye end as five pronounced crowns. The eye basin may be pinched together, puckered or unevenly bumpy, characters that are important and usually constant. Some varieties have a ring of five small bumps called beading around the eye.

The green calyx that surrounds the eye is more variable. The eye may be open or closed by the sepals. Sometimes the sepals themselves are a useful feature. They may be upright around an open eye, or long, green and reflexed.

Skin

Five characters are important;

The presence or absence of **wax**, but this depends on the ripeness of the fruit and whether or not it has been lying for a time in the grass.

The position and quantity of **russet,** such as the distinct russet patch around the eye in Brown Snout which is instantly recognisable or russet spreading as a network or patches over the cheek as in Fillbarrel.

The background colour of the **skin**; usually yellow or green.

The conspicuousness of the **lenticels**. The small breathing pores on the skin that may be sometimes corky, black or even coloured.

The type, colour and quantity of the **flush**. It may be diffuse, flecked or striped. The amount of flush will again vary with season and the amount of sunshine that gets to the fruit. It is likely to be a lot less, sometimes absent altogether, in fruit from old, densely shaded trees.

Internal characters

Such details as the core, the tube and the colour and texture of the flesh are more variable. An identification should not rely heavily on these factors, but use them to confirm the more stable evidence.

Check list

It is a good idea to observe and note down all these characters before going to the key. It is also handy later on if you have made a record to refer to when another sample comes along that could be the same variety.

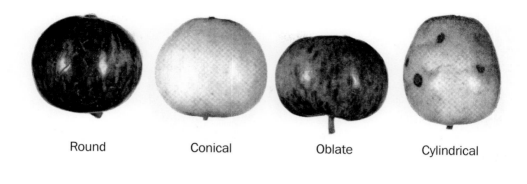

| Round | Conical | Oblate | Cylindrical |

| Flattened-conical | Elongated-conical | Conical-cylindrical | Flattened-cylindrical |

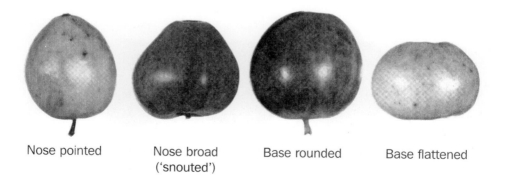

| Nose pointed | Nose broad ('snouted') | Base rounded | Base flattened |

Fruit shapes

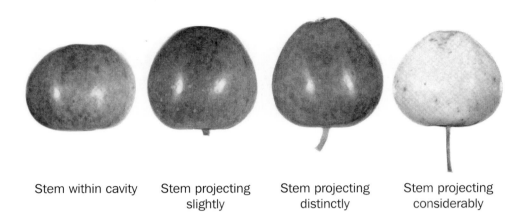

| Stem within cavity | Stem projecting slightly | Stem projecting distinctly | Stem projecting considerably |

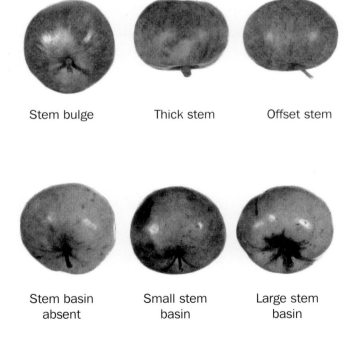

Stem bulge   Thick stem   Offset stem

Stem basin absent   Small stem basin   Large stem basin

Stems and Noses

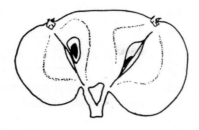

Keys to Identification of Apples for Cider

The following keys should help you to sort out the identity of your apple sample. There are three separate keys that suit the distinct characteristics of the varieties to be found in each county. Since they vary so much between more westerly locations, it is best to try the appropriate one first, failing that, try the main Key A.

Key A – Varieties found in Somerset, Hereford and parts of Devon
1. Bittersweet Apples
2. Bittersharp Apples
3. Sharp and Dual Purpose Apples
4. Pure Sweet Apples

Key B – West Dorset varieties

Key C – Devon, Dorset and Cornish varieties
1. Sharps, Bittersharps, Dual Purpose and Dessert Apples
2. Sweet and Bittersweet Apples

Key A – VARIETIES FOUND IN SOMERSET, HEREFORD AND PARTS OF DEVON

Key A: 1 Bittersweet

Shape	Strongly flushed, predominantly diffuse	Lightly flushed and usually striped	Flush absent or slight
Elongated conical	Brown Thorn Don's Seedling Tremletts Bitter Stable Jersey	Improved Dove Dove	Michelin Brown Thorn
Flattened conical	Ashton Brown Jersey Burrowhill Jersey Dabinett Red Jersey Norton Bitters Pennard Bitter Somerset Redstreak Vilberie	Coat Jersey Stembridge Jersey Pennard Bitter Vilberie	Bulmers Norman Brown Snout Michelin Vilberie White Jersey
Conical	Ashton Bitter Ashton Brown Jersey Balls Bittersweet Black Dabinett Chisel Jersey Red Jersey Harry Masters Jersey Stable Jersey Tremletts Bitter	Coat Jersey Dove Improved Dove Major Norton Bitters Stembridge Jersey White Close Pippin Yarlington Mill	Bulmers Norman Brown Snout Late Gold Medaille d'Or Michelin Nehou White Jersey
Cylindrical	Ashton Brown Jersey Fillbarrel Norton Bitters	Hangdown	Hangdown Improved Hangdown Silver Cup

Key A: 2 Bittersharp

Shape	Strongly flushed, predominantly diffuse	Lightly flushed and usually striped	Flush absent or slight
Flattened conical	Kingston Black Porters Perfection	Lorna Doone	Lorna Doone
Conical	Cap of Liberty Porters Perfection Tom Tanners	Stembridge Clusters Breakwells Seedling	
Cylindrical	Black George Cap of Liberty Foxwhelps Kingston Black	Stembridge Clusters	
Oblate	Lambrook Pippin	Lambrook Pippin	
Round	Stoke Red	Breakwells Seedling	

Key A: 3 Sharp and Dual Purpose

Shape	Strongly flushed, predominantly diffuse	Lightly flushed and usually striped	Flush absent or slight
Elongated conical	Wear & Tear	Pig's Nose Sheep's Nose	Cider Lady's Finger Stubbard
Conical or Flattened conical	Backwell Red Crimson King Katy Kings Favourite Langworthy Red Tom Putt Ten Commandments	Sheep's Nose Tom Putt Twenty Pip	Fair Maid Taunton Gin Yeovil Sour Reinette Obry Sheep's Nose Blenheim Orange Gennet Moyle
Cylindrical	Backwell Red Browns Apple Imp. Kingston Black Sops in Wine	Imp.Lambrook Pip. Long Tom	Gin Stubbard Blenheim Orange
Oblate	Browns Apple Crimson King Ten Commandments Vallis		Buttery Dor Fair Maid Taunton Belle de Boscoop Reinette Obry
Round	Langworthy Sops in Wine	Improved Lambrook Pippin	

Key A: 4 Pure sweet varieties

Shape	Strongly flushed, predominantly diffuse	Lightly flushed and usually striped	Flush absent or slight
Elongated conical or cylindrical		Bell	
Conical	Dunkertons Late	Le Bret Taylors Sweet	Morgan Sweet Sweet Alford Sweet Coppin White Alphington
Cylindrical	Dunkertons late	Le Bret Taylors Sweet	Sweet Coppin White Alphington
Oblate	Court Royal Slack-ma-Girdle	Slack-ma-Girdle Woodbine	
Round	Court Royal		

Key B: WEST DORSET APPLES

1.	Fruits falling early September	Stubbard
	Most fruits falling in October or later	2
2.	Sharp or bittersharp	3
	Sweet or bittersweet	13
3.	Flush absent or slight	4
	Flush diffuse or striped	9
4.	Tannin noticeable	5
	Tannin faint or absent	6
5.	Skin dry and scabby, very sharp taste	Marnhull Mill
	Skin waxy, often russeted. Pronounced tannin	Dashayes Crab
6.	Yellow when ripe	7
	Staying green when ripe	8
7.	Rounded, long stem. Citric acidity	Tangy
	Conical, slightly crowned, russeted, short stem	Golden Ball
8.	Large, oblate, early dual purpose	Buttery Dor
	Small, rounded, hard, very late maturing	Ironsides

9.	Flush predominantly diffuse or slightly striped	10
	Flush markedly striped, early maturing	12
10.	More than 2/3 bright scarlet, oblate	Kings Favourite
	Less than above	11
11.	Large, cylindrical, late keeping dual purpose	Blenheim Orange
	Medium-large, flattened conical, mid-season	Fair Maid of Devon
12.	Irregularly furrowed, crowned nose tall, bright red/yellow	Warrior
	Smooth eye basin, flecked & striped dark red	Browns Apple
13.	Tannin pronounced	14
	Tannin absent or slight	20
14.	Flush absent or slight	15
	Flush strong, usually striped and flecked	Dabinett
15.	Stem long, protruding distinctly	16
	Stem short or a stub within the cavity	19
16.	Green no flush. Tall conical, rather waisted, narrow nose, 10 ribs	Tom Legg
	Greenish-yellow. Small, rounded, often russeted, slight flush	Golly Knapp
	Green. Pinched & ribbed nose, flush rare. Late	Winter Stubbard
17.	Eye basin small or slight	18
	Eye basin usually well defined often crowned	19
18.	Medium, yellowish. Usually flushed orange, often considerable russet	Loders
	Small-med, green. Eye basin often absent, occasionally beaded. Few red dots	Meadow cottage
19.	Med-large. Yellowish-green, pinkish/orange flush, russet around the eye	Marlpits Late
	Large. Pale greenish-yellow. Crowned conical, conspicuous russet dots	Golden Bittersweet
20.	Flush absent or slight	21
	Flush often strong and striped	22
21.	Yellow, diffuse pinkish flush. Long thin stem	Sweet Alford
	Greenish-yellow, often mauvish flush. Short, stout stem	Sweet Coppin
22.	Flattened conical/cylindrical or oblate	Slack-ma-Girdle/Woodbine
	Tall, conical and waisted	Bell
	Tall, tending to cylindrical	Northwood

Key C: DEVON, DORSET AND CORNISH APPLES

Key C: 1 Sharp, Bittersharp, Dual-Purpose and Dessert Apples

Shape	Strongly flushed, predominantly diffuse	Lightly flushed and usually striped	Flush absent or slight
Elongated conical	Plum	Cornish Aromatic Pigs Nose Tommy Knight	Nine Square Stubbard
Flattened conical	Kings Favourite [Crimson King]	All Doer Colmans Seedling Fair Maid of Devon Netherton Late Blower Ponsford Tommy Knight Tom Putt Warrior	Dufflin Glass Apple Hockings Green Killerton Sharp Payhembury Polly Ponsford Tan Harvey Yeovil Sour Cadbury
Conical	Devon Quarrenden	Colloggett Pippin Paignton Marigold Twenty Pip	Dashayes Crab Golden Ball Marnhull Mill
Oblate	Captain Broad Devon Crimson Queen	Don's Delight Netherton Late Blower Ponsford	Buttery Dor Captain Broad Payhembury Plympton Pippin Ponsford
Round or elliptical	Langworthy Plum		Cornish Longstem Ironsides Tangy
Cylindrical	Ben's Red Kings Favourite [Crimson King]	Blenheim Orange Paignton Marigold Tommy Knight	Dufflin Hockings Green Polly Stubbard

Key C: 2 Sweet and Bittersweet Apples

Shape	Strongly flushed, predominantly diffuse	Lightly flushed and usually striped	Flush absent or slight
Elongated conical or cylindrical	Bridge Sweet Kingston Bitter Tale Sweet	Killerton Sweet Northwood	Golden Bittersweet Golly Knapp Halstow Natural Listener Loders Marlpits late Meadow Cottage Sercombes Natural Spotted Dick Sweet Bay Tom Legg White Alphington
Conical	Ellis Bitter Tale Sweet Tremletts Bitter	Bell Killerton Sweet Northwood	Golden Bittersweet Golly Knapp Loders Marlpits late Meadow Cottage Sercombes Natural Sweet Alford Sweet Bay Sweet Coppin Tom Legg White Alphington
Cylindrical		Northwood	Listener Spotted Dick Sweet Coppin
Round	Sweet Blenheim Kingston Bitter		Halstow Natural
Oblate	Bridge Sweet Tale Sweet Sweet Blenheim Slack-ma-Girdle	Killerton Sweet Slack-ma-Girdle Woodbine	Halstow Natural

Alphabetical List of Cider Apple Descriptions

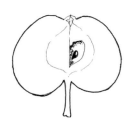

ALL DOER

Mid-season Dual Purpose Cider Apple

Although there are no written records of its origin, All Doer seems to be a variety that is local to Exeter and rarely seen elsewhere. It is not a true cider apple and was never brought to Long Ashton for a trial, but the trees are reputedly very scab resistant, a useful feature especially for organic growing. It flowers in early May.

All Doer is noticeable for its handsome, shiny, bright scarlet and yellow striped fruits that are ready mid October.

Fruit: Medium to large, 45–55mm. Flattened conical with a broad base and nose. Stem short [10mm] but just showing from a deep cavity. Eye small and closed in a shallow, slightly puckered basin. Skin smooth and shiny yellow, always more than 60% covered with strong red stripes, but more yellow and less striped around the eye.

Cider: No fruit, juice or cider notes ever appeared on the Long Ashton records.

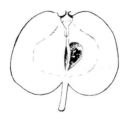

ASHTON BITTER

Early Full Bittersweet Cider Apple

This seedling, raised from a Dabinett x Stoke Red cross by Mr G T Spinks, plant breeder at Long Ashton in the 1950s was a big hope carrying many of the attributes of both varieties. It was resurrected in the 1980s from a trial orchards at EHS Rosemaund, Hereford where it had been cropping well and was widely planted as an early harvesting variety for intensive bush orchards. It was intended to spread the harvesting season forward into late September but never fulfilled its potential and for several reasons it quickly fell out of favour. Many bush trees were replaced or top-worked with a better variety but it may still be found occasionally.

The bushy head is made up of weak, whippy lateral branches covered in numerous greyish-green, willowy leaves making it difficult to train to ideal bush tree shape. It crops biennially and is susceptible to mildew though free from scab. Flowering late May with Dabinett and Stoke Red, it needs a pollinator variety close by.

The apples mature in late September or early October and are highly coloured, bright orange-red and glossy when ripe.

Fruit: Medium-large, 55–>60mm. Conical, rounded; regular, tending to ribbed; king fruits common. Stem thick, projecting distinctly from a small, shallow cavity; fleshy and often strigged in king fruit. Eye basin small, narrow, deep, rather irregular or beaded; sepals fairly long but often broken, reflexed at tips. Skin golden yellow, smooth, waxy or greasy; russet none or very little near stem. Always flushed more than 75%, orange diffuse flecked and speckled bright red. Flesh full bittersweet; yellowish, juicy and chewy. Core tube large, deep, usually open to core.

Juice: SG 1060

Cider: The juice is full bittersweet with plenty of astringency and a good aroma, producing a full bittersweet cider with rather strong tannin but useful for blending.

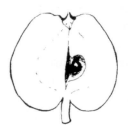

ASHTON BROWN JERSEY

Late Medium Bittersweet Cider Apple

Synonym: Brown Jersey

This typical Somerset 'jersey' apple was found as an un-named variety in an old cider orchard in Long Ashton village in the early 1900s. In its preliminary trials it was called Ashton No. 32. It was properly named later when its excellent vintage cider making characteristics became recognised, but it never achieved popularity as an orchard tree because it is so slow to come into cropping. It was planted in a few old standard and bush trial orchards in both Hereford and Somerset. Ashton Brown Jersey forms a medium sized tree with a compact head. It is fairly scab resistant and once it does come into cropping, it is quite regular. Flowering is mid-season.

The fruit matures late, from the second week of November onwards. It is rather small, regular shaped, dark red-brown and rough russeted.

Fruit: Medium, rather small, 45–55mm. Blunt nosed conical tending towards cylindrical; regular. Stem often fleshy, projecting slightly or level with the base; stem cavity regular, usually shallow but sometimes deep. Eye basin shallow or slight, slightly puckered or trace of beading; calyx closed or slightly open, sepals reflexed, sometimes green. Skin yellow or yellowish-green to golden yellow or orange; overall rough and dull; light russet often considerable, spreading in a network, but sometimes only in the stem cavity; lenticels conspicuous, often very large and irregular especially round the stem. Flush always more than 35% often more then 65%, flecked or slightly striped, rarely diffuse only, dark red flecks and stripes. Flesh sweet and astringent; yellowish or white, sometimes greenish; woolly.

Juice: SG 1054; acidity 0.14%; tannin 0.23%

Cider: Ashton Brown Jersey produces a good, full-bodied cider, soft and medium bittersweet.

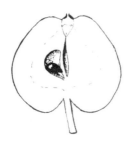

BACKWELL RED

Mid Season Sharp Cider Apple

At the beginning or the century this variety was widely grown in north Somerset and is named after the village of Backwell where it probably still exists as old trees. Early trials at the Cider Institute confirmed its vintage value and many trees were distributed in county trial orchards. It has since lost favour owing to its irregular cropping, though it may be more reliable when grown as a bush tree. Mature standard trees are medium sized with a neat compact head, but are slightly scab susceptible. Bush trees can be very vigorous and spreading. Spurring is rather sparse with much bare wood. Cropping is slow to establish and rather biennial, but good. It flowers early mid-season, late April to early May, is diploid and a good pollinator. Although the fruit matures fairly early, from the second week of October, it is often difficult to shake off the trees until late October.

The apples are medium sized, rounded, red and yellow and characterised by a long stem in a curiously flattened, one-sided stem cavity.

Fruit: Small, often medium, 40–50mm. Conical or tending to cylindrical, rarely tending to round; regular. Stem projecting distinctly or considerably, thin and woody and sometimes offset; stem cavity medium, often deep and characteristically flattened on one side. Eye basin medium, puckered, sometimes ribbed, sometimes irregular and beaded, occasionally flattened on one side; calyx slightly open or closed, sepals fairly long and reflexed but usually broken. Skin pale yellow or greenish-yellow; smooth and slightly waxy; rarely rough and scaly russet spreading across the cheek; lenticels sometimes conspicuous. Flush always present, usually more than 75%, often more or less complete, diffuse red flecked and slightly striped. Flesh acidic with no astringency; white, usually reddened under the skin and in the vascular bundles, soft and juicy.

Juice: SG 1051; acidity 0.70%; tannin 0.13%

Cider: Backwell Red cider at best is good, sharp, light and fruity. It can often rather thin and of average quality and is best blended. Fermentation is moderately slow.

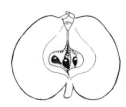

BALL'S BITTERSWEET

Scab Resistant Mild Bittersweet Cider Apple

Synonym Balls Apple, EB 54 in NF Collection, Brogdale. [Not EB 52, a bittersharp selection from the same stable]

This variety was raised in Herefordshire by E Balls in 1950s from a cross between Medaille d'Or and the reputedly scab resistant Old Foxwhelp. Ball's Bittersweet is gaining some popularity since it seems to have inherited its parent's scab resistance which is holding at the moment. Likely to be found almost exclusively as new plantings, it makes a good moderately vigorous tree, well spurred and precocious in cropping. Flowering mid-late May.

The large, bold red striped fruits with a stub of a stem are ready early-mid October.

Fruit: Medium to large size 45–60mm. Shape conical with a small narrow nose, rounded with a hint of ribs. Stem thick, woody, very short, usually within the small but deep cavity or level with the base. Eye basin small, usually smooth; eye slightly open, sepals often green, tips reflexed. Skin smooth, becoming waxy, yellow-green to naples yellow, always half to two thirds covered with strong dark red stripes over a crimson or orange flush. Some russet in the stem cavity and occasional patches or streaks spreading from the eye. Flesh juicy but chewy, yellowish, often reddened under the stripes and vascular strands pink.

Juice: Mild bittersweet.

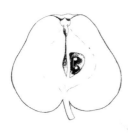

BELL APPLE

Mid Season Sweet Cider Apple

Synonyms: Sweet Sheep's Nose, Belle Apple

It is its distinctive shape that gives this Somerset sweet apple its name. Bell Apple or Sweet Sheep's Nose is one of many Sheep's Noses, but is different enough to be distinguished as a distinct variety with its dark mauve flush and sweet taste. Bell was first recorded at the RHS Exhibition in 1883 and it was quite often sent to Long Ashton from central Somerset where it may have arisen. Bell makes a useful cider with good flavour and aroma, and was therefore quite a popular choice in old farm orchards. It still occurs as old trees throughout central and southern Somerset down to west Dorset. Mature Bell trees are quite large and upright but tend to droop with heavy crops. Flowering time is late April or early May.

The apples are distinctly bell-shaped, large and green, conical, with a broad, flat base and a stubby stalk. They are ready for harvest in late October.

Fruit: Often large to very large but varying with crop, 45–more than 60mm. Conical, base broad and flat, usually slightly waisted nose; smoothly ribbed or angular. Stem a stout stub within a broad, deep cavity, occasionally projecting slightly. Eye basin small but well defined, smooth; calyx open, sepals free, upright, distinctive. Skin pale green; smooth, dry; russet light in the stem cavity; lenticels with pale surround. Flush usually 50–75%, speckled and flecked pinkish-mauve to red. Flesh mild sweet; chewy greenish.

Juice: SG 1058; acidity 0.18%; tannin 0.12%

Cider: Long Ashton cider trials describe Bell as a very useful sweet cider with good flavour and aroma, good alone or blended. Fermentation is slow.

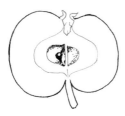

BELLE DE BOSCOOP

Sub-acid Dual Purpose Apple

This 19th century dessert apple from Boscoop in the Netherlands became popular in England from around 1920 and was once widely propagated. It is a good sound variety that makes a large tree carrying often very large fruit. They are not handsome enough and rather too sharp for present day dessert taste, but they cook well and the variety has remained fairly popular. It crops up in the West Country since Showerings cider company propagated it for their new orchards in the 1970s and also frequently offered it as a prolific juice variety to other suppliers and colleagues. Belle de Boscoop is a triploid variety, hence the large trees and fruit. It has attractive blossom flowering mid-season but it may not be much use as a pollinator.

The large, distinctly oval, greenish-yellow fruit are covered with grey russet. Ready late, October-November.

Fruit: Often large to very large 55–>60mm. Flattened round, oval; fairly regular in section. Stem project slightly [10mm] from a narrow russeted cavity. Eye closed in a wide puckered basin. Skin bright yellow but showing indistinctly through a grey russet covering. Usually with a scarlet flush. Flesh rather acid, definitely aromatic; firm, yellow to cream, crisp.

Juice: Probably rather acidic but with a good sugar content.

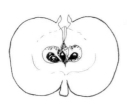

BEN'S RED

Sub-acid Dessert Apple

This is an early 19th century Devonshire dessert apple, a seedling from Red Quarrenden and Farleigh Beauty that was once grown widely in the county for the table market. Although striking in appearance, it has little character and is no longer commercially important. But it is still popular in the county, several nurseries list it and does go to make some cider. Ben's Red trees are sturdy and dwarf and have a reputation for producing great crops of fruit.

The bright red apples are flushed dark red with darker stripes and rather a flat shape.

Fruit: Small-medium [45–55mm]. Flattened cylindrical; slightly ribbed. Stem short [10mm] in a narrow, green russeted cavity. Eye basin broad and shallow. Eye usually open , sepals green. Lenticels as russet dots. Skin pale yellow, smooth, waxy or greasy, usually almost entirely covered in a rich dark red flush, striped darker red. Occasionally appears more yellow with wide red stripes. Flesh fine, crisp, sweet; yellow, sometimes tinged red.

Juice: Sweet, but not likely to contribute much character to cider.

BICKINGTON GREY

Sharp Cider Apple

The home if this curiously shaped pale russeted apple is not far from Newton Abbott in one of Devon's best cider growing areas. It occurs locally occasionally as old trees in farm orchards. It has become more well known recently and is now being regularly propagated by several nurseries. Trees flower mid-season and the fruit is ready by mid October.

The apples are pale yellow, sometimes with a distinctive curl-tail, and heavily netted with golden russet to give it a greyed appearance on the tree.

Fruit: small to medium size, 45–55mm. Oblate or cylindrical, base sometimes with a swollen bump; rounded in section, occasionally lopsided. Stem a tiny stub in an almost non-existent cavity. Eye basin small, narrow, gently crowned and irregular. Eye open, sepals long, upright, reflexed at the tips. Skin pale primrose covered in a very distinctive network of light brown russet spreading from the eye over more than half of the fruit. Flesh sharp, white.

Juice: SG 0152; acidity 0.70%; tannin 0.15%

Cider: This is a typical Devon sharp apple and although there are no Long Ashton records, it is likely that it would make a would contribute a good traditional flavour.

BLACK DABINETT

Late Bittersweet Cider Apple

Synonyms: Tommy Rodford

Tommy Rodford apples were recorded at the Bath and West show in 1897, from Kingsbury Episcopi in central Somerset and some trees were recently found still standing in an old orchard in the village. This apple is probably a sport or a seedling of the true Dabinett but it is rather more robust. In the mid 1980s it was thought that it might have some potential for bush orchards and so was propagated on a small scale. Young trees are flourishing under the name Black Dabinett in some recent trial orchards, but it is rather late maturing and for that reason, it is unlikely to become fashionable at the present time. But its fruit has excellent vintage quality and it is a variety that deserves to be more widely planted.

Black Dabinett trees are vigorous and spreading but well spurred. The variety should crop well as bush trees. Flowering is late mid season with Dabinett and Chisel Jersey.

The fruit is a similar shape to the true Dabinett but it matures a bit later, well into November. It can be distinguished from it by its darker, purple-brown flush often covered with an attractive network of russet and dots, and by the curious whitish patches which occur on some fruits.

Fruit: Medium, 45–55mm. Conical tending to oblate; rounded, sometimes angular. Stem often off-set, projects distinctly, from a deep, often slightly furrowed cavity; just a stub in king fruits. Eye basin small, slightly furrowed; calyx closed. Skin dark green, with lighter patches; dry; russet usually in distinctive spreading network. Flush always, 50% to nearly complete, diffuse and slightly flecked dark purple-red. Flesh bittersweet; dry, chewy; strongly greenish, vascular strands green.

Juice: SG 1048; acidity 0.23%; tannin 0.28%

Cider: Recorded in 1908 as *'a sweet, fairly full flavoured cider of pleasant taste and aroma.'* Although it could be used alone, it was described as too bitter, and best for blending.

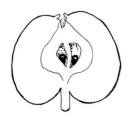

BLACK GEORGE

Mild Bittersharp Cider Apple

One of several old cider apples local to Gordano, Portishead and neighbouring Gloucestershire where elderly trees can occasionally still be found. George was a generic name for a group of crab apples selected overtime for taste. [A george is an old name for a drinking vessel.] Some were named after the village or area where they originated, such as Chiswell George but there were also Black and Red Georges, even a Royal George. The Black George described here is similar to the description by Thomas Hogg in his Fruit Manual for Black Crab in the 19th century.

Black George apples, ready mid October, are rather rounded with virtually no eye basin and flushed very dark red with brighter strips.

Fruit: Size 45–60mm, smaller on old trees. Flattened cylindrical or round, slightly ribbed at the shoulder. Eye basin shallow or slight, relatively smooth or shallowly crowned. Eye open or closed. Stem just a stub in the cavity. The base colour is yellow-green but more that 75% covered with a dark red flush and short bright red stripes with a scattering of small russet dots. Flesh is chewy, yellowish and sharp tasting.

Juice: SG 1050; acidity 0.30%; tannin 0.22%

Cider: Hogg said of Black Crab *'the fruit make a good cider, good enough to be kept for the master's drinking'*. From Long Ashton's 1932 cider: Fairly pleasant and well balanced. Rather coarse tannin.

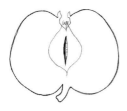

BLENHEIM ORANGE

Late Keeping Multi Purpose Apple

Blenheim Orange is really an old fashioned table apple, a fruit excellent for both dessert or baking, a noble sauce apple of legendary repute. It was a chance seedling found growing close to the wall of Blenheim Park in around 1740 and nurtured by Mr Kempster of Old Woodstock. It was first called Kempster's Pippin but as its worth soon became apparent and nurseries began to propagate it, the Duke of Marlborough *graciously allowed its name to be changed* to Blenheim Orange. Its fame quickly spread and it was the winner of many prizes in the early 19th century. It is still found growing in many parts of England, especially in the grass orchards of the West of England where it thrives on stone brash and calcareous soil and has surely contributed its good qualities to many a gallon of West Country cider. Being a triploid variety it grows vigorously into a large, strong limbed, flat headed tree. It is slow to settle into cropping and may only yield a good crop every other year. Blenheim flowers in early May but its pollen is poor. Trees will need a suitable mid season flowering pollinator until they pass middle age.

Blenheim Orange apples are large, sometimes difficult to hold in one hand, orange flushed green-golden and very russeted.

Fruit: Large, 55–>60mm. Flattened conical or cylindrical with a rounded base and broad nose; rounded in section. Stem thick, sometimes just a stub in a narrow, deep cavity, sometimes projecting slightly. Eye basin variable, often deep with bumpy irregular shoulders. Eye wide open with short green sepals. Skin often dry and rough with heavy patches and spreading streaks of golden russet. Lenticels conspicuous as small brown or red dots. Ground colour golden yellow-green, about half covered with dark orange flush, slightly striped and flecked bright red. Flesh sub-acid, juicy and melting with a good flavour.

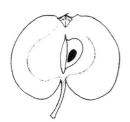

BREAKWELL'S SEEDLING

Early Bittersharp Cider Apple

This variety originated in Pethyre Farm, Monmouth and was propagated by George Breakwell at the end of the 19th century. It occurs sparsely in orchards planted in the 1950s and '60s in Hereford and occasionally as an early harvesting variety in bush orchards in Somerset. Mature trees are medium sized, upright and easily distinguished by their luxuriant, darkly curled foliage. Should be scab resistant. Breakwells is a good early mid-season pollinator.

The rather small, roundish, striped fruits are ready to drop by the end of September but they are easily bruised and quickly rot.

Fruit: Medium or small, 40–50mm. Flattened conical or conical-cylindrical; somewhat irregular. Stem projecting considerably from a usually deep cavity. Eye basin usually slight, shallow; corona of beads usual. Eye closed. Skin smooth, waxy, yellow to greenish-yellow. Scab resistant. Always about two-thirds flecked and striped dark red. No diffuse flush. Flesh mild sharp, sometimes slightly astringent; white, occasionally reddened, soft, juicy.

Juice: SG 1042; acidity 0.64%; tannin 0.23%

Cider: Medium bittersharp, rather thin and light. Only average quality.

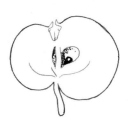

BRIDGE SWEET

Mid-season Sweet Cider Apple

Probably the same as Horell's Sweet.

A sample of fruit was sent to Long Ashton in 1955 from Horell & Son, of Bridge Farm, Stoke Cannon, Exeter. As a protégé from the cidermaker himself, it must have been rated worth a trial but sadly there are no records of cider made from it. But judging by the juice sample, it is a pure sweet with almost no tannin and rather low in sugar. Bridge Sweet probably remains as a local variety occasionally found in the Exe valley.

The apples are very rounded and regular, part covered with a rather dull brownish-red flush. They mature by mid October but rot quickly.

Fruit: Medium to large, 45–60mm. Flattened, rounded oblate, rounded in section. Stem projecting slightly or distinctly from a deep, russeted cavity. Eye basin smooth, shallow, sometimes slightly crowned, eye often open. Skin light green. Lenticels sometimes noticeable on the flush. Always half to completely flushed with brownish red-purple. Flesh pure sweet; white.

Juice: SG 1049; acidity 0.21%; tannin 0.08%

Cider: Unfortunately there are no LARS comments on the 1955 sample.

BROWN'S APPLE

Early Sharp Cider Apple

This apple was bred at Hill's Nursery, Barkington Manor near Staverton in Devon, probably around 1895. It was one of several similar varieties intended for traditional Devon orchards, clean, fresh tasting sharps. Brown's Apple is very similar to its sister, Paignton Marigold. Both were until recently, free from scab. For this reason, Brown's Apple has also been very popular in Somerset both for replanting old orchards and for use in more recent bush orchards where it has been extensively used from the late 1990s as a trouble-free, early maturing variety. It is commonly seen now in all counties and is capable of phenomenal crops, even if biennially. It is a first quality sharp apple but was not always classed as a cider apple in the past, and has not always commanded a premium price. This is happily not the case with the modern contract bush orchards where it is welcomed.

Young trees are slow to start growth in the first year or so, but once established, become very vigorous with many rather upright primary branches. They can be prone to canker and mildew. Spurring is slow with some bare wood in the first years. Brown's Apple flowers mid season. Blossom is bold but slow to develop. Standard trees are medium sized with a slightly spreading, neat head.

The apples are distinctive; bright red, rather broad and flattened and quite a generous size.

Fruit: Medium to large, 45–60mm plus. Oblate or flattened cylindrical, broad; regular. Stem thick, fleshy, often strigged, often off-set, projecting distinctly from a deep, steep cavity. Eye basin medium, smooth with a trace of ribs; calyx slightly open, sepals long, pubescent. Skin yellow, shiny, waxy; russet absent. Always more than 65%, often almost completely flushed, heavy diffuse, flecked and striped dark red. Flesh mild sharp, white, chewy.

Juice: SG 1048; acidity 0.67%; tannin 0.12%

Cider: Brown's Apple makes a very good, slightly scented sharp cider, fresh and clean, with a fruity aroma.

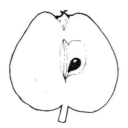

BROWN SNOUT

Late Bittersweet Cider Apple

Brown Snout is a Hereford variety sometimes seen in orchards in the South West. It is said to have originated on a farm at Yarkhill in the middle of the 19th century. It is now widely distributed in the West Midlands since it has been propagated and distributed by Bulmers. It was also included in the 1952 series of bush tree trial orchards in all the cider growing counties. Because of its late flowering habit Brown Snout is useful for low-lying areas or frost pockets and is often found growing alongside Vilberie as a pollinator. Mature trees are medium sized with upright growth similar to Michelin but it is a far less commonly grown variety.

Brown Snout apples are similar in appearance to Michelin but have a distinctive russet patch around the eye and are a regular conical shape without ribs. The are mature by the first half of November

Fruit: Small, rarely medium, 40–55mm Conical, rarely rounded or cylindrical. Stem thin, woody, projecting slightly from a medium sized, narrow cavity. Eye basin absent or slight; calyx closed, sepals touching, short, reflexed at tip. Skin yellow-green, smooth slightly waxy; russet at stem and eye, sometimes slightly spreading to cheek; lenticels sometimes small brown dots. Rarely flushed a slight diffuse pinkish-orange. Flesh sweet with slight astringency; white, soft, dry.

Juice: SG 1053; acidity 0.24%; tannin 0.24%

Cider: Mild to medium bittersweet; soft astringent tannin, average quality.

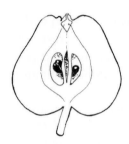

BROWN THORN

Late Mild Bittersweet Cider Apple

Probably a Hereford variety, limited numbers of Brown Thorn were planted in that county in the 1957 series of Long Ashton trial orchards. Later, in the 1960s, more were planted in Somerset but it has never gained much popularity. Mature trees are large to medium sized with an untidy spreading head. It was deemed a promising scab resistant variety that crops well and would be useful for its late maturing fruit. It flowers late but is diploid and a good pollinator.

Brown Thorn fruits are medium sized, conical and yellow-green with a brownish-red flush, sometimes heavily russeted.

Fruit: Medium, 45–55mm. Rather elongated conical with a flattened nose and rounded base; regular tending to ribbed. Stem often off-set and/or strigged, usually showing distinctly from a small cavity often flattened on one side. Eye basin medium size, puckered, occasionally beaded. Skin green to yellow-green, smooth and dry. Usually half flushed brownish-red, flecked and striped bright red. Often heavily rusted, scaly in the stem cavity. Flesh white.

Juice: Mild bittersweet.

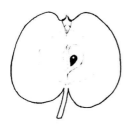

BULMERS NORMAN

Early Bittersweet Cider Apple

When Bulmer's Cider Company began to establish orchards in the early 20th century, this was one of the many varieties that were imported from France. It was un-named at first but because of its outstanding orchard performance, it was propagated and widely distributed as Bulmer's Norman. It is now grown throughout the West Country and is one of the best, most frequently used stem-builders. Because of its vigour, this variety sometimes out-grows the top worked variety and it is not uncommon to see tree canopies, part Bulmer's Norman, part a weaker variety, or totally taken over by Bulmer's Norman. It occurs commonly in its own right throughout Somerset, mostly in standard orchards.

The trees are often easy to spot; large, very vigorous and spreading, often with a span of up to 40 feet, and with broad, distinctive scab spotted leaves. Interestingly the leaves are usually free from scab in off years when the trees are not carrying fruit. It flowers early mid-season but is a triploid and therefore a poor pollinator.

Its apples, often disfigured and distorted with scab, are large, broadly conical and plain yellow-green. They mature and drop in the first half of October but are thin skinned and do not keep at all well. They are distinguished from similar looking Morgan Sweet by their harsh tannic taste.

Fruit: Medium to large, 55–more than 60mm. Conical sometimes flattened; somewhat irregular. Stem thin, woody, projecting slightly, sometimes distinctly, sometimes level with base; stem cavity very wide and deep. Eye basin often very deep, usually irregular, sometimes puckered. Skin yellow to green; smooth, slightly waxy; russet usually confined to stem cavity, rarely spreading to cheek; lenticels sometimes conspicuous. Flush rare, sometimes a slight patch of diffuse orange. Flesh sweet with full tannin; green, woolly.

Juice: SG 1053; acidity 0.24%; tannin 0.27%

Cider: Medium bittersweet; hard and bitter tannin. Fast fermenting juice.

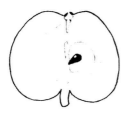

BURROW HILL EARLY

Early Bittersweet Cider Apple

In the search in the 1980s for early maturing cider varieties with potential for bush orchards, Burrow Hill Early was recovered by Julian Temperley of Burrow Hill Cider, as an unknown variety from an old orchard in nearby Stembridge and named after the local landmark. Although it was propagated by Long Ashton for use in bush orchards, it was never widely adopted because it is very slow to come into cropping and rather biennial. It still exists as old trees and in a few recent bush trial orchards. Bush trees are vigorous and spreading with much bare wood. Flowering is mid season.

The strongly red flushed apples are ready by the end of September or early October and make a useful to start the pressing season.

Fruit: Medium, 40–55mm. Rounded conical with a broad flat base. Stem within or protruding slightly from a small shallow cavity. Eye basin shallow, slightly puckered or smooth; sepals closed or slightly open. Skin pale yellow, smooth and waxy; lenticels surrounded by light patches on the flush near the stem end; russet occasionally spreading over the cheek. Flush always more than 60%, flecked and slightly striped, bright red. Flesh sweet and astringent; white, dry, chewy, soft.

Juice: Full bittersweet. SG 1055

Cider: Burrow Hill Early makes an excellent full bodied, early bittersweet cider with a very fruity aroma and fair tannin. It is said to be useful alone or for blending with inferior ciders.

BUTTERY DOR
Early Multipurpose Apple

Synonyms: Buttery Door, Do, d'Or or Dough. Perhaps even Buttleigh Dor

Buttery Dor fruit was first sent to the Cider Institute in 1926 by Mr Warren, cider maker of Netherbury in Dorset. It is often called a pastry apple, one suited to making apple dumplings, sharp and well flavoured. It is a variety that is reputed to have been brought over by monks from Normandy in the 16th century. An old tree, well known locally as Buttery Dor, was discovered in a derelict orchard in North Bowood, Dorset. It was saved by an enthusiast, Fred Thirlby, who took a cutting to Romsey in the late1950s. Some time later Mrs Scott Daniel took a cutting from her uncle's tree and brought the variety back to Bridport. Buttery Dor has recently been re-propagated from that tree and is now widely available. Occasional tall, vigorous old Buttery Dor trees can still be found in that part of West Dorset.

The apples are a good size, rather flattened shape, pale green or golden, and mildly sharp tasting.

Fruit: Medium to large; often more than 60mm. Oblate; often lopsided, angular or tending to ribbed. Stem medium to short, woody, within a medium cavity, broad and deep. Eye basin small, deep, rather irregular, occasionally beaded; sepals short and closed. Skin butter yellow, bright acid yellow green when unripe; smooth, waxy; very slight russet in eye and stem cavities, occasionally spreading in patches and veins. Flush absent. Flesh mild sharp; rather mealy, yellowish.

Juice: SG 1046; acidity 0.77%; tannin 0.14%

Cider: When it was first tried at Long Ashton in 1926, Buttery Dor cider was described as '*fair with an aromatic flavour but fermentation is too fast.*'

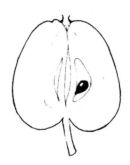

CAP OF LIBERTY

Mid-season Full Bittersharp Cider Apple

Synonyms: Red Soldiers, Bloody Soldier

This was once a well known and popular vintage quality apple that has always been highly recommended for cider making. Scott's nursery catalogue recorded it in 1873. It is a variety originating in the Martock area where it was grown in moderate numbers in the 19th century. It still exists as single trees in other parts of Somerset. Cap of Liberty would have been planted in more recent bush orchards but for its propensity to disease, its poor tree habit and the small size of its fruit. Cap of Liberty trees are moderately vigorous, unwieldy fastigiate with multiple leaders consisting of several long, unbranched, spreading limbs. It is a good, somewhat irregular cropper, preferring heavy, limestone derived soils. It is also rather susceptible to scab, water core, canker and apple sawfly. It comes with a definite health warning to potential growers! It flowers in late April or early May.

The small apples are broadly conical with a non-existent eye basin and prominent brown lenticels on the pinkish-red flush. Ready by mid October.

Fruit: Small, 40–45mm. Conical-cylindrical, rounded nose and base. Stem slender, woody, projecting distinctly from a small, narrow cavity. Eye basin slight or absent; eye beaded and puckered, slightly irregular; calyx usually open. Skin yellow-green, dry, slightly rough; susceptible to scab which often disfigures the fruit; lenticels conspicuous as small, brown dots especially on flush, often associated with russet patches. Flush always, 50% or more, diffuse pinkish red flecked with bright red. Flesh sharp with light tannin; juicy, chewy and yellowish.

Juice: SG 1055; acidity 0.92%, tannin 0.30%. Its high acid content sets it apart as a 'balanced' juice

Cider: Cap of Liberty makes a rich acid cider of excellent quality and body, with a good clean, fruity taste. Fermentation can be slow. Highly recommended as a vintage variety.

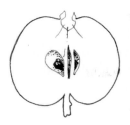

CAPTAIN BROAD

Late Dual Purpose Apple with some Tannin

Synonyms: known locally as Captain Smith or John Broad

The variety listed in the National Fruit Collection as Small's Admirable appears to be genetically identical to the Cornish Captain Broad.

Captain Broad is now propagated by several nurseries and found throughout Cornwall, Devon and West Dorset. Like a large irregular, coloured Bramley, this 'dumpling apple' is associated with the name John Broad who probably lived near Fowey in south Cornwall and where numerous trees are still found. They have been grown extensively in the Golant area for at least 150 years and keep their good reputation as one of the best Cornish cider apple varieties. In Cornwall Captain can mean squire or 'boss' as well as sea-captain. This variety, like many other very old varieties, is a 'pitcher', one that will root from a cutting with burr knots. Trees are big, vigorous and Bramley-like, growth is predominantly late in the season. Flowering in early May.

The apples, ready mid-late October, are medium sized, pale yellow green with a dull red-brown flush and a long stalk..

Fruit: Medium-moderately large, 44–>60mm. Oblate or flattened cylindrical, strongly ribbed, with a broad flat nose and broad base. Stem usually long in a neat, deep cavity with a little russet. Eye slightly open with sepals upright in a narrow furrowed and crowned basin. Skin pale yellow-green getting lighter on the base, usually half covered with a deep pink/brown maroon flush with a few russet dots. Flesh greenish, juicy with a mild sharp culinary taste and a hint of tannin.

Useful for both cider making and cooking. One of the best Cornish cider apples.

CHISEL JERSEY

Late Full Bittersweet Cider Apple

Synonyms: Sidestalk, Bitter or Chesil Jerseys or Jersey Chisel

For more than 100 years the true Chisel Jersey, which originated in the Martock area, has been popular in Somerset, but it was not known outside its native county until the 1960s. Scott's Catalogue of 1893 quotes it as *'perhaps the most esteemed bittersweet sort in the Somerset orchards . . . mixed with rich, sweet kinds ripening at the same time, it produces a cider of unequalled goodness.'* Chisel Jersey occurs frequently in bush orchards planted in the 1970's in Somerset and Dorset for Taunton Cider Company. It has rather lost favour since it is very scab susceptible and frequently produces small cracked and severely russeted fruits. Bush trees of Chisel Jersey easily form a natural centre leader shape. They are fairly precocious and crop annually but flower very late in May. Although it is a good pollinator itself, it is not self fertile and needs to be cross pollinated. Its half sister variety, Dabinett, which is one of the few varieties still flowering at the same time, is unfortunately incompatible and fruit set can be disappointing. Standard trees are large and semi-spreading.

The fruit which matures late, from November on, is conical with a dark brownish-pink flush, often heavily cracked with scab. Its offset stem is a useful character.

Fruit: Variable in size, medium, often small especially if russeted, 40–55mm. Rounded conical, broad nose and base; regularly rounded. Stem projecting distinctly or slightly, fairly thick and woody, offset, strig frequently present; stem cavity medium or small, shallow, usually flattened on one side. Eye basin small, shallow and usually slightly puckered, corona sometimes present; calyx tightly closed, sepals touching, fairly long and reflexed, slightly pubescent but usually broken. Skin greenish-yellow or yellow; smooth, slightly waxy; russet usual but variable, sometimes very severe and associated with cracks and distortion which severely reduced the size of the fruits, frequently the russet is patchy or forms a fine net over the cheek of the fruit. Flush always present to about 65%, diffuse and flecked brownish-pink or red. Flesh sweet and astringent; white, woolly and dry.

Juice: SG 1059; acidity 0.20%; tannin 0.45%

Cider: Strong, rich, high colour. Full bittersweet with astringent tannin, full bodied and of good quality, but it needs to be blended.

CIDER LADY'S FINGER

Early Mild Sharp Cider Apple

Lady's Finger is probably a generic name for varieties with fruits which are shaped longer than broad, elliptical and elongated. There are many Lady's Fingers from various places, notably Hereford. This West Country one has a little tannin in its juice and qualifies as a cider apple although it is probably more interesting as a curiosity. The tree is compact and moderately vigorous, often drooping with fruit. It flowers in the second half of May, and crops biennially, the fruit maturing by early October.

The elongated fruit is a distinctive elliptical shape, plain yellow green with no flush and characteristic long stem. There is often a curious, fine, hair-like ridge running across the cheek from eye to stem.

Fruit: Medium, 45–55mm. Elliptical; rounded, regular. Stem long, slender, woody, projecting distinctly; stem cavity absent or very slight. Eye basin absent or very slight, eye beaded or slightly irregular; calyx closed, sepals short, reflexed at tips. Skin yellow to yellow-green, smooth and waxy; russet absent; lenticels with a pale surround. Flush absent. Core large, open, elliptical with few viable seeds. Flesh mild sharp with some tannin, rather non-descript; juicy, melting; greenish, browning rapidly when cut.

Juice: SG 1052; acidity 0.59%; tannin 0.12%

Cider: This Lady's Finger makes a thin but pleasantly light, medium brisk cider with a fair aroma and flavour but lacking in body. It has moderate value for blending.

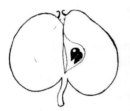

COAT JERSEY

Late Full bittersweet Cider Apple
Synonym: possibly Twistbody Jersey

This variety originated in the village of Coat, near Martock in Somerset before the twentieth century. Since early 1970s it has been widely planted in bush orchards for Taunton Cider in Somerset and Dorset, where it crops heavily but biennially. Coat Jersey trees are typically strong, upright and spreading. They produce sturdy growth that is sparsely spurred and often with much bare wood. The variety is also very prone to scab and in most years the fruit is badly marked and miss-shaped. It flowers mid season and is a good pollinator for other varieties. The fruit on young trees is carried in clusters close to the main branches.

The apples are small, pale green and red striped, conical in shape and with a distinctive long stalk. It not ready until late October or early November.

Fruit: Small-medium, 40–55mm. Conical or flattened conical; tending to ribbed. Stem woody, projecting considerably from a deep cavity. Eye basin usually deep and puckered, often with ribbing extending from eye to cheek, calyx usually slightly open, sepals often reflexed at tip. Skin pale greenish yellow; smooth; russet in stem cavity only. Very scab susceptible. Flush always present, up to 30%, dark red striped. Flesh sweet and astringent; white, sometimes greenish below the skin, woolly.

Juice: SG 1047; acidity 0.18%; tannin 0.27%

Cider: Coat Jersey makes a full bodied bittersweet cider with a good character. Its aroma and flavour are good but it is too astringent alone and best blended.

COLEMAN'S SEEDLING

Late Mid-season Sharp Cider Apple

Synonyms: Hathway, Coleman's Prolific

Trees of this variety is still sometimes found in the favoured area between Newton St Cyres and Exeter, and up the Exe valley to Whiteways old orchards at Whimple and even in east Devon. It is now propagated by several nurseries and deserves to be more widely planted. Tree growth is fairly vigorous and healthy, at first upright but tending to droop after cropping. Crops are heavy and consistent. It is reputedly pest and disease free although the Long Ashton samples in the 1950s recorded some scab on the fruit. Flowers late mid-season.

The apples are medium sized, rounded and greenish-yellow with a pinkish flush. Ready mid-late October.

Fruit: Small to medium, 40–55mm. Flattened conical with a small nose and rounded base. Sometimes rather lopsided with a trace of ribs. Stem medium [10mm], projecting slightly or distinctly from a small but deep russeted cavity. Eye basin small, narrow and shallow, slightly furrowed and crowned. Eye slightly open. Sepals short, free. Skin yellow to yellow-green. Occasionally russet patches or streaks. Always half covered with a crimson-orange diffuse flush with short flecks and stripes of bright red. Flesh sharp; white, chewy.

Juice: SG 1044; acidity 0.65%; tannin 0.13%. Sugar content low.

Cider: Pleasant, brisk and light. Described in its first trial at Long Ashton as '*. . . one of the best in the mild sharp group*'. Fermentation slow.

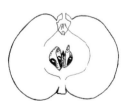

COLLOGGETT PIPPIN

Mid-season Dual Purpose Apple

Synonyms: Cornish Giant, Lawry's Cornish Giant

This variety came from Collogett Farm [pronounced 'cloggit'], Botus Fleming, Cornwall, named after John Lawry, a well known 19th century horticulturalist, although it is believed by some to have been raised by Jack Creber who is said to have grown the original tree from cider pomace on his farm. It is a popular variety, now propagated by several nurseries and to be found in Cornwall, Devon and West Dorset. Its trees are wildly spreading with much bare wood, but regular cropping. It can be canker susceptible. In a good year the fruit is surprisingly pleasant to taste, if you can take a little tannin, but they probably overstate their reputation as the '*best cider apple in the district*'. Flowers mid-late May.

Colloggett apples are unmistakably large, angular, knobbly, cream and red striped. Season, early October.

Fruit: Large or very large, 55–>60mm. Conical with a small pinched nose and a rounded base. Very angular and distinctly ribbed from top to bottom. Eye basin small, narrow and deep, furrowed with many crowns. Eye open with upright sepals. Stem thick, within the large, broad and deep cavity or projecting slightly. Skin smooth and waxy, pale green going creamy yellow when ripe and always half coloured with short bright red stripes and flecks. Flesh greenish, juicy and melting, pleasantly sharp tasting, not 'culinary', and with slight bitterness.

Juice: SG 1040; acidity 0.32%; tannin 0.20%

Cider: Very good, dry light. It has been said that it makes a 'champagne' or 'ladies' cider.

CORNISH AROMATIC
Sub-acid Dessert Apple

This well known and popular variety, said to have been discovered in a cottage garden near Truro at around 1800 but it may well be much older. It is an apple that can crop up in any garden or orchard in the West Country and it must often have contributed to the cider harvest. It is an old fashioned, rather sharp tasting dessert apple but, at its best, it does have a good, spicy aromatic flavour that might contribute something to the cider in a good year. It is a vigorous growing tip-bearer but reported to be a light cropper.

The handsome bright red, russeted and speckled apples are ready mid October but improve with keeping.

Fruit: Medium-large [50–60mm]. Conical to oblong-conical or oval; distinctly ribbed, occasionally irregular . Stem medium in a narrow cavity. Eye closed in a deep, irregular, ribbed basin. Sepals long. Skin greenish-yellow ripening to gold. Much russet network and streaks, lenticels conspicuous as brown dots. Flushed bright or dull red, striped and streaked. Flesh sweet; firm, crisp, cream coloured.

Juice: Good high sugar content and a spicy aromatic aroma that may come over into the juice.

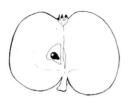

COURT ROYAL

Late Pure Sweet Cider Apple

Synonym: Sweet Blenheim, Pound, Pound Apple, Improved Pound

Mature trees are found throughout Somerset and east Devon where it is often known as Sweet Blenheim. At the beginning of the twentieth century Court Royal was sold in many industrial areas as a dessert apple, following Morgan Sweet into the markets. It is pleasant tasting and crisp but no longer has any commercial appeal and is just used for cider making. Few new trees are planted except as replacements in old orchards. Mature trees are large, vigorous and spreading. Court Royal is a triploid and its vigour was often exploited as a stem builder for top-working with other weaker varieties. The grafts frequently re-grow in old trees to produce a head of Court Royal intermingled with the original variety. Young trees are slow to bear but settle down to crop well, although this variety is rather prone to brown rot and scab.

The apples are large and green with an orange flush and distinctive upright sepals. It is not ready for harvest until early November but may start falling in October and begin to rot.

Fruit: Usually large, usually more than 60mm. Flattened spherical, sometimes oblate; sometimes irregular. Stem thick and fleshy, within a variable, shallow to deep cavity. Eye basin usually very deep, smooth and sometimes irregular; calyx usually open, sepals upright, fairly long, free, green at the base, pubescent. Skin yellow or greenish-yellow, smooth with very little wax; sometimes slight russet in the stem cavity; lenticels usually not conspicuous, but sometimes large and irregular in the stem cavity where they may be surrounded by a white or dark green patch. Flush always present, about 60% diffuse orange, flecked and occasionally slightly striped with dark red. Flesh pure sweet; white or slightly greenish, slightly crisp.

Juice: SG 1050; acidity 0.21%; tannin 0.11%. Full bodied, sweet.

Cider: Court Royal ferments quickly to a pure sweet cider.

DABINETT

Late Full Bittersweet Cider Apple

Dabinett was found as a 'gribble', a self-sown seedling, probably a seedling of Chisel Jersey, in a hedge in Middle Lambrook, Somerset by Mr William Dabinett, from a local Somerset family. It was propagated extensively by Charles

Malus sylvestris

All Doer

Ashton Bitter

Ashton Brown
Jersey

Backwell Red

Ball's Bittersweet

Bell Apple

Belle de Boscoop

Ben's Red

Black Dabinett

Black George

Blenheim Orange

Bickington Grey

Breakwell's
Seedling

Bridge Sweet

Brown Snout

Brown Thorn

Brown's Apple

Bulmers Norman

Burrow Hill Early

Buttery Dor

Chisel Jersey

Captain Broad

Cap of Liberty

Cider Lady's Finger

Coat Jersey

Coleman's
Seedling

Colloggett Pippin

Cornish Aromatic

Court Royal

Dabinett

Dashayes Crab

Devon Crimson
Queen

Devonshire
Quarrenden

Don's Delight

Don's Seedling

Dove

Dufflin

Dunkertons Late

Ellis Bitter

Fair Maid of Devon

Fair Maid of
Taunton

Fillbarrel

Foxwelps

Gennet Moyle

Gin

Glass Apple

Golden Ball

Golden Bittersweet

Golly Knapp

Halstow Natural

Hangdown

Harry Masters
Jersey

Hockings Green

Improved Dove

Improved
Hangdown

Improved Kingston
Black

Improved
Lambrook Pippin

Ironsides

Katy

Killerton Sharp

Killerton Sweet

Kings Favourite

Kingston Bitter

Kingston Black

Lambrook Pippin

Langworthy

Late Gold

Le Bret

Listener

Loders

Long Tom

Lorna Doone

Major

Marlpits Late

Marnhull Mill

Meadow Cottage

Morgan Sweet

Michelin

Médaille D'Or

Néhou

Netherton Late
Blower

Nine Square

Northwood

Norton Bitters

Paignton Marigold

Payhembury

Pennard Bitter

Pig's Nose

Plum Apple

Plympton Pippin

Polly Whitehair

Ponsford

Porter's Perfection

Red Jersey

Reinette Obry

Sercombes Natural

Severn Bank

Sheep's Nose

Silver Cup

Slack-Ma-Girdle

Somerset Redstreak

Sops In Wine

Spotted Dick

Stable Jersey

Stembridge
Clusters

Stembridge Jersey

Stoke Red

Stubbard

Sweet Alford

Sweet Bay

Sweet Cleave

Sweet Coppin

Tale Sweet

Tan Harvey

Tangy

Taylors

Ten
Commandments

Tom Legg

Tommy Knight

Tom Putt

Tom Tanners

Tremletts Bitter

Warrior

Vallis Apple

Vilberie

Twenty Pip

Wear and Tear

White Alphington

White Close Pippin

White Jersey

Winter Stubbard

Woodbine

Yarlington Mill

Yeovil Sour

Porter, nurseryman of East Lambrook where there are still some fine trees. It is common in standard and bush orchards throughout all the cider growing counties because of its well justified reputation for good and regular crops. It holds top place for the most popular and highly esteemed variety today.

Dabinett trees are usually small with a neat rounded head. Their vigour is only moderate and the final tree size depends very much on the soil type and conditions. Bush trees are very susceptible to soil potash deficiency. Young trees are moderately vigorous with plenty of lateral branches at good angles, but leader growth is weak and may quickly loose dominance. Older standard trees may be short lived due to a sensitivity to virus infection. Characteristically Dabinett will produce secondary blossom which may appear at any time of the year, even in the autumn, but their normal flowering period is late mid season. The variety has become slightly susceptible to both mildew and scab in bush orchards, although it seems fairly resistant in old farm orchards.

The fruit which matures in early November, is medium sized, rounded, conical and heavy, with a dark red flecked and striped flush.

Fruit: Medium, sometimes small, 40–55mm. Flattened conical, sometimes round; regular; very occasionally fruits are twinned. Stem thin and woody, projecting slightly, sometimes distinctly from a small cavity, narrow at the base, sometimes shallow, particularly in king fruits. Eye basin usually slight and shallow, slightly puckered or smooth; calyx tightly closed, sometimes slightly open, sepals short. Skin yellow or greenish yellow; smooth and waxy; russet slight in stem cavity, spreading to cheek; lenticels not usually apparent but sometimes large, corky and conspicuous. Flush always present, usually more than 65%, flecked and slightly striped pinkish-red with extensive diffuse background. Flesh sweet and softly astringent; greenish or white; slightly crisp.

Juice: SG 1057; acidity 0.18%; tannin 0.29%

Cider: Dabinett cider is usually high quality and well balanced, full bittersweet but with a soft astringency and full bodied. It is suitable for blending or using alone as an excellent single variety cider for the connoisseur.

DASHAYES CRAB

Full Bittersharp Cider Apple

The old walled orchard at Dash Hayes in Kington Magna may have existed from the time that the 18th century house was built, its name referring to the then owner of the land. Many of the trees will have been replanted over the years and probably most of the original varieties will have perished some time ago. More recently the remnants of the collection, probably dating back to the turn of the 20th century and clearly planted to serve both the kitchen of the house and the annual cider making, have been reduced further by the ravages of hungry sheep. The last two remaining trees of a row carry small yellow and very astringent tasting fruit. As an unknown variety, we named it Dashayes Crab. There are still some good varieties growing alongside; Tanners, Golden Ball and Sour Cadbury.

Both trees were small, with moderate vigour and compact rounded heads. Our young trees from the DATA Project in the nursery were also compact with a few short feathers. Their leaves are large, oval with irregular crenulations on the margins.

The apples which are ready early mid season, are small, yellow and waisted conical 'jersey' shape with corky lenticels.

Fruit: Small-medium, 45–55mm. Conical, slightly waisted with a small flat node and broad flat base; rather ribbed in section. Stem variable length [5–10mm], projecting slightly or distinctly from a small cavity. Eye basin small, shallow, tending to crowned and occasionally beaded. Sepals closed. Skin slightly waxy. Some russet occasionally spreading in streaks, lenticels corky or sometimes coloured. Colour yellow-green ripening to yellow. Frequently with a trace or more of diffuse orange. Flesh very sharp, chewy, greenish.

Juice: Extremely astringent, like crab apple.
SG 1068; acidity 0.54%; tannin 0.98%

Cider: Should make a good extender.

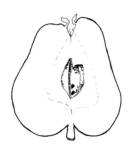

DEVON CRIMSON QUEEN

Dual Purpose Early Dessert

This is not a cider apple but it is an old and popular variety that often occurs in south west Devon up to the Cornish border. It may very well be the same as the Cornish apple Queenie which was a favourite apple in St Dominic near Botus Fleming and once grown extensively in the Tamar valley in the old days. It is good eating and does have a little tannin in its juice in some years. It flowers late April to early May.

The fruits are a beautiful dark red with a plum-like bloom, shiny when polished. They are ready in late August and keep well for a few weeks.

Fruit: Medium-large size, 50–60mm. Cylindrical, sometimes oblate, slightly ribbed in section. Stem short [10mm] just showing from a deep, narrow cavity. Eye basin shallow, slightly puckered and gently crowned. Eye more or less closed, sepals green. Skin tough with a waxy bloom. Lenticels conspicuous white dots. Always more or less overall covered with deep, purple red flush. Flesh sweet, sub acid, sometimes with a little tannin; white, stained red under the skin.

Cider: Rather too early and not a true cider apple by any means but the apples have a little astringency that makes a small contribution to flavour.

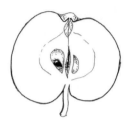

DEVONSHIRE QUARRENDEN

Sub-Acid Dessert Apple

This is a very old and well known apple with many other names that was introduced into England in the 17th century. A popular and much grown apple especially in gardens, often for its attractive appearance and its reputed aromatic strawberry flavour. The trees are medium sized, crop abundantly and will tolerate wind and rain but are prone to scab and canker. It flowers mid-season but its blossom is sterile therefore it needs a good pollinator.

The distinctive red flushed, crowned fruit are ready in August or September

Fruit: Small-medium [45–55mm]. Flat, broad nosed, conical; regular, sometimes ribbed. Stem short [10mm] often within a deep, russeted cavity. Eye closed in a broad basin with distinct crowns. Skin pale-mid-green, smooth, dry and covered with much spreading patches and streaks of russet, especially on the flush. Lenticels small brown dots. Always up to half covered with a dark, maroon red diffuse flush. Flesh sharp, good flavoured, juicy, a little chewy, greenish.

Juice: Sub-acid and useful for sugar and flavour. Rather too early for cider making but it could go for an early Christmas cider.

DON'S DELIGHT

Mid Season Sub-Acid Cooking Apple

This is a relatively new apple, a chance seedling discovered in a garden in Torquay. Its potential was spotted by Don Cockman who grew it from grafts in the late 1980s. It was introduced in 1996 by Kevin Croucher at Thornhayes and is now propagated as a reliable, if not outstandingly flavoured cooker. The trees are large and growth is vigorous and clean. It is ideal for growing in the wet West Country weather, especially for those who want to remain pesticide free, since it is resistant to scab and canker. It crops well and regularly and is gaining in popularity, mainly as a garden variety. The blossom is very pretty in early May.

The red and green striped apples can be exceptionally large. Ready by September/October but will keep well.

Fruit: Large-very large [55->70mm]. Flattened conical, often more or less oblate; strongly ribbed from the eye downwards, often lopsided. Stem fairly long, projecting distinctly from a deep cavity, filled with scabby, gold ochre russet. Eye basin rather small, pinched, 2 or more crowns, rather furrowed. Eye open. Skin pale green-yellow-green, smooth, slightly greasy. Lenticels conspicuous on the flush. Always about half flushed orange, flecked and speckled bright red with thin red stripes, especially on the base. Flesh sub-acid, rich flavoured; crisp, juicy, greenish, aroma good.

Juice: Pleasantly sub-acid. Could be useful for its sugar content.

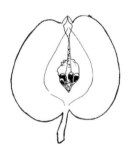

DON'S SEEDLING

Early Bittersweet Cider Apple

This apple was raised by Don Wilson at Long Ashton Research Station in around 1960. He chose an un-named scab resistant Canadian seedling, 49-121 and made several crosses with Tremletts Bitter. The best, most scab resistant offspring was named after him. Like most Tremletts Bitter seedlings it has inherited many of its parent's characters and the fruit of both are almost identical. Don's Seedling has recently been introduced as young trees which have a reasonable growth habit and are moderately vigorous with a good centre leader. But like Tremletts, the fruits are borne in heavy clusters, the branches tending to weep with crop, suggesting a tendency for a pattern of biennial cropping to develop. Slightly susceptible to mildew. Flowering in early May.

The handsome bright red, heavily flushed conical fruit are ready by the end of September or early October.

Fruit: Medium size 45–60mm. Cylindrical to conical with a small nose and rounded base, rather ribbed in section. Stem long [10–15mm], projecting distinctly from a small, shallow russet-free cavity. Eye basin small, even slight, tending to crowned. Eye usually closed with upright sepals. Skin smooth, glossy, waxy. Base colour is pale green but more than 60% covered with a heavy bright-dark red flush. Flesh medium bittersweet; greenish, chewy.

Juice: Strongly bittersweet and similar flavour to Tremletts Bitter.

Cider: Likely to be very useful.

DOVE
Late Medium Bittersweet Cider Apple
Synonym: Pennard Dove

Dove is probably a very old variety which was first recorded by the Bath and West in 1899. It is likely to have originated in Glastonbury, at the once famous nurseries on the side of the Tor and is frequently found in old orchards in that area of Somerset where is still known as Pennard Dove. It was very popular at one time because of its late flowering habit which suited the frost susceptible, low lying orchards of that area, but has become more and more prone to scab and virus, so has consequently lost its popularity. There are a number of more recent introductions which have been named after it, for example Improved Dove, Late Dove and Stone Dove. Some are scab-free but none inherit the good qualities of Dove's juice. Small numbers of Dove were included in a few orchards planted for Taunton Cider Company in the early 1970s.

Dove itself forms a distinctive tree. It is small with dense, well spurred, drooping branches and rough, greyish foliage. As a bush tree it is small and densely branched. It is precocious and cropping can be regular and heavy but its performance is variable with district and disease. Dove flowers in late in May, is diploid and a good pollinator.

The apples are small conical and rather waisted with a broad base. They become extremely waxy when they are really mature, which is not before the first week of November.

Fruit: Small to medium, 40–50mm. Waisted, conical, rarely conic-cylindrical, base broad. Stem thick, usually woody, within the cavity or level with the base, rarely projecting slightly; stem cavity variable, medium, usually shallow, sometimes deep. Eye basin usually medium and shallow, sometimes slight, rarely deep, puckered, frequently ribbed, often slightly beaded; calyx tightly closed, sepals touching, often overlapping, fairly long, reflexed at tip, usually broken. Skin green or yellowish-green; smooth and very waxy; russet confined to stem cavity, heavy and scaly, occasionally spreading to cheek; lenticels inconspicuous except on bruises, occasionally dark green. Scab susceptible. Flush always present but variable, usually 30–65%, lightly flecked and slightly striped red over a little diffuse, rarely striped only. Flesh sweet, usually with some astringency, pleasant flavour; white, yellowish or greenish-white; slightly woolly and juicy.

Juice: SG 1049; acidity 0.22%; tannin 0.31%

Cider: Dove cider is mild bittersweet and only rather average quality but with good body, soft tannin and a pleasant flavour. Sugar content is often below average and fermentation slow.

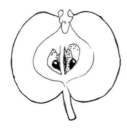

DUFFLIN

Bittersharp Cider Apple

Renowned for its high sugar content, Dufflin was included in some of the Long Ashton 1957 trial orchards. A sample of fruit came to the Research Station in 1906 from Truro and others from Crediton and Totnes in the 1950s. It is certainly an old variety, recorded by the Woolhope Society [1878–83]. There is a similar variety, a very old dual purpose, sub-acid apple called Devon Russet [Devonshire Buckland or even Lily Buckland.] This is more flattened oblate, a pale cream colour, heavily russeted and usually with just a stub of a stem.

Dufflin trees are medium sized, ungainly and vigorous, producing much bare wood on branches that are upright at first then drooping with heavy crops. It is subject to canker but crops are good with a tendency to biennial. It probably deserves to be planted more widely. Flowers early May.

The rounded yellow fruits of Dufflin have a long stem and are easily distinguished by their russet patches and streaks. Ready early October.

Fruit: Medium-large size, 45–60mm. Rather flattened conical or cylindrical and rounded in section. Stem projects distinctly from a small, deep cavity and sometimes has a bulge or strig at the base. Eye basin small, shallow, slightly puckered. Eye usually open with upright sepals. Skin pale yellow, dry with corky lenticels and considerable russet, often heavy and spreading from the stem and the eye as a network or patches across the cheek. Rarely there may be a hint of orange flush. Flesh mild bittersharp, citric, very sweet and quite pleasant; juicy, yellowish, blotting paper texture.

Juice: Many samples with characteristically high sugar levels. SG 1050–1074; acidity 0.90%; tannin 0.20%

Cider: Rich and full bodied. Clean with a good aroma and flavour. Too sharp alone, valuable for blending. Fermentation slow.

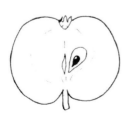

DUNKERTONS LATE

Late Sweet Cider Apple

Synonym: Dunkerton's Sweet

This apple was raised by Mr Dunkerton, of Baltonsborough, near Glastonbury in the 1940s, probably from a seedling saved from pomace. It has been adopted in a limited way for traditional orchards, especially in its home area and can be found growing and cropping well as youngish or middle aged standard trees. Dunkerton's Late is fairly vigorous and often forms a very big, but well spurred tree. It is robust and fairly disease resistant with some potential as a late harvesting variety, but it has never become popular for bush orchards because of its late ripening season. Flowering late mid-season.

The apples are broad shouldered, cylinder-shaped, yellow with an orange flush, but they are often harvested too early when still green with a mauveish flush. It is not really ready until late November

Fruit: Medium, 45–55mm. Cylindrical tending towards conical, broad nose and broad rounded base; rounded or slightly oval in section. Stem often a woody stub within the cavity or projecting slightly; stem cavity medium, narrow, deep. Eye basin medium, broad and shallow, smooth or slightly bumpy, tending to crowned; calyx wide open, sepals free, short, green. Skin smooth and dry; russet usually confined to stem cavity, golden; lenticels conspicuous pale surround, milky on unripe fruits. Colour cold pea green but primrose yellow when ripe. Flush always present, variable, up to 70% diffuse or speckled pinkish-mauve to brownish red. Flesh sweet; very firm, chewy; pale yellow or greenish with green vascular strands.

Juice: SG 1047; acidity 0.22%; tannin 0.09%

Cider: A sweet, light and fruity cider.

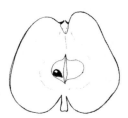

ELLIS BITTER

Early Bittersweet Cider Apple

Incorrect synonym, Honiton Early

Ellis Bitter is an east Devon variety which was distributed outside the county in some of the Long Ashton trial orchards planted in the 1930s. It is enjoying recent popularity as an early maturing bittersweet, growing and cropping with some success in a number of new bush orchards planted during the late 1990s. Mature standard trees are frequently large with a spreading habit and slow to come into crop. Young bush trees are fast growing and rather upright but respond to training and will produce a good centre leader. Once they settle down to forming fruiting spurs, cropping is fairly regular and the fruit is heavy. It is slightly prone to scab but not mildew. Flowering time is mid May. Fruit is ready late September, one of the earliest traditional varieties to mature in modern bush orchards.

Ellis Bitter apples are large and bold, covered in a heavily flecked flush which sometimes has a bluish tinge. They do not keep well and are often attacked by birds attracted to their bright shiny skin, which makes them rot even more quickly.

Fruit: Large, rarely medium, usually more than 60mm. Conical, base flat, nose pointed; sometimes tending to ribbed. Stem thick, often slightly off-set, often with a bulge at spur end, level with the base or projecting slightly from a narrow, deep cavity. Eye basin well defined, often deep and irregular; calyx slightly open, sepals short, often green and pubescent. Skin yellow to greenish-yellow; smooth, waxy; russet slight; slight scab. Flush always present, virtually complete, always heavily flecked and striped dark red, sometimes with a purplish tinge, diffuse background sometimes absent in patches. Flesh sweet and astringent; white; crisp and juicy.

Juice: SG 1053; acidity 0.20%; tannin 0.24%

Cider: A good quality medium bittersweet with soft, astringent tannin, rather thin on its own and better blended.

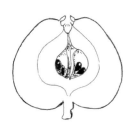

FAIR MAID OF DEVON

Mid-season Sharp Cider Apple

Once widely grown in east and mid Devon but not so common elsewhere. It was also included in some of the Long Ashton bush trial orchards of the 'thirties and may be found in their remnants. Fair Maid has gained more recent popularity as a good sharp and is frequently propagated as standard trees. Standard trees are medium sized with a compact habit, heavily spurred even on the main branches. Bush trees are moderately strong with a dominant centre leader but spreading and drooping with crops which are often heavy. The numerous prominent lenticels on the wood are a characteristic. The variety is susceptible to scab and woolly aphis. Flowers mid-season, first two weeks of May.

Fruits are large and distinctively flushed bright red. Matures early-mid October but fruit is very susceptible to sawfly and brown rot and keeps poorly.

Fruit: Medium to large, 45->60mm. Flattened conical with a flat base. Stem often thick and woody, projecting slightly from a broad deep cavity. Often with a bulge at the end in king fruits. Eye basin broad, shallow and puckered or slightly irregular. Eye often open, sepals reflexed and long. Skin smooth, slightly waxy, greenish-yellow with occasional patches of russet, always partly, sometimes fully covered with a bright red flush, flecked and striped dark red. Scab susceptible. Flesh sharp with little astringency; white to pale yellow, juicy, melting and soft.

Juice: Yield is high but sugar content often low.
SG 1050; acidity 0.95%; tannin 0.11%

Cider: Thin, dry and sharp, body light. Fermentation rapid. Described by Long Ashton as '. . . *only fair vintage quality but fills the bag*'

FAIR MAID OF TAUNTON

Mid Season Mild Sharp Cider Apple

Synonym: Moonshines or Moonlight, Greasy Butcher

This variety is described by Hogg in the 19th century as a dessert apple, but not of the first quality. It was recorded in the National Apple Register in 1831. Although it was only infrequently sent in for cider making trials, it made an agreeable though rather characterless cider. Its juice is quite high in acid and described as rather 'Devon type', a flat, mild sharp. It is still found in old orchards in south and central Somerset and north Dorset where it is usually called Moonshines. It is said to have got its name because its pale yellow apples shine in the moonlight and can still be seen to be picked up after dark! Trees are large, tall and spreading. Flowering time is early May. It is rather scab susceptible.

The apples are large, rounded and conspicuously butter yellow when ripe come mid to late October.

Fruit: Large to medium, 40–55mm. Oblate or conical; rounded, ribbed on body, sometimes rather irregular. Stem short, thick and fleshy, occasionally strigged, projecting distinctly from a small, shallow cavity. Eye basin shallow, often broad, slightly irregular and beaded; calyx often open, sepals broad, flat, reflexed. Skin pale green or whitish, turning butter yellow; smooth, dry, greasy when ripe; russet sometimes heavy in stem cavity and spreading netted over the cheek; lenticels sometimes corky with a pale surround on immature fruit, often with a red or brown dot when ripe. Flushed with a hint of red on sunny side to about 30%, diffuse, speckled or flecked, pink or pinkish orange. Flesh sharp with some astringency; white or yellowish, tender, juicy, chewy.

Juice: SG 1047; acidity 0.55%; tannin 0.19%

Cider: Moderately sweet with some acidity, Fair Maid of Taunton makes a cider with a fairly agreeable aroma and flavour, but lacking in character.

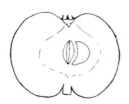

FILLBARREL

Late Mid Season Bittersweet Cider Apple

Most old records come from the Woolston, Sutton Montis, Wincanton area of south east Somerset and over the border into north Dorset where a few old trees can still be found. Fillbarrel is probably a late 19th century apple. It was included in the Long Ashton trial orchards planted in 1957, and subsequently in a few orchards planted for Taunton Cider in 1970s. Mature trees are vigorous, spreading and densely branched. Young trees can be poorly spurred with much bare wood. Although it can crop heavily, Fillbarrel is very biennial and fill the barrels only every other year. It is very early flowering, at the end of April or early May, and unlike most cider apples, occasionally gets caught by late frosts. It is best planted in a frost free spot since if the flowers are damaged the crop can be lost.

The attractive fruit is a neat cylindrical shape, dark red flushed and covered with a distinctive network of golden russet. It is mature from mid to late October.

Fruit: Medium, 45–55mm, can be very small with heavy crops. Cylindrical; usually rounded sometimes lopsided. Stem a thick stub within the small, tight, deep stem cavity. Eye basin large, broad and deep, smooth; calyx open, sepals short, free in an upright crown. Skin yellow green; rough and dry; russet heavy round eye basin, spreading all over as a golden network; lenticels conspicuous, russeted. Flush always 30–65%, diffuse scarlet flush with crimson flecks and some stripes. Flesh mild bittersweet; yellowish, crisp, juicy, chewy.

Juice: SG 1062; acidity 0.25%; tannin 0.30%

Cider: Fillbarrel makes a good medium cider, full bodied and with well marked astringency.

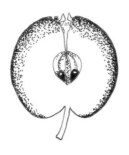

FOXWHELPS

A Group of Mild Bittersharp Cider Apples

Including Red, Broxwood, Improved and Bulmers Foxwhelp

The Old Foxwhelp described in *Apples and Pears as Vintage Fruit* in 1851 was thought most likely to be a 17th century Forest of Dean apple. Brilliant red and with a rough peculiar flavour, Hogg reports that the cider 'is not fit for drinking till the second year, but then very good'. Perhaps its rough sharpness is best modulated by a little malo-lactic fermentation as is also the sharpest Kingston Black cider.

Although this Foxwhelp and its relations are natives of Hereford and Gloucestershire there have been plantings of several of them in the past in trial orchards further south. Red Foxwhelp was included in the 1950s and Improved, in the plantings before 1920. More recently Red, Broxwood and Bulmers Foxwhelp have begun to gain some popularity with specialist cidermakers as early maturing bittersharps with some character. Mature trees are medium to large sized and rather upright. The leaves of some are characteristically small, rounded, curled and wavy.

The fruits of this group of apples are easily distinguished by their extreme acidity and markedly striped, bright red flush and long stem. Their shape is often irregularly cylindrical, their eye basin virtually non-existent and usually beaded.

Fruit: Size variable, medium-large. 45–60mm. Rounded, elliptical, or cylindrical with a rounded nose and base; often lopsided and with a tendency to ribbed. Stem often long, 12–25mm, green, usually projecting distinctly from a small, shallow cavity. [Broxwood's cavity is usually broad and deep]. Eye basin very slight or non-existent, fairly smooth and frequently beaded. Eye often more or less open, sepals short, green. Skin smooth, waxy, occasionally some russet in the stem cavity, perhaps spreading slightly. Lenticels sometimes small brown dots. Colour, pale butter yellow, always almost completely covered with a bright red 'Worcester' flush, strongly flecked and striped darker red. Flesh usually mildly bittersharp with some astringency and a pleasant clean flavour juicy; chewy, yellowish, often reddened under the skin.

Juice: Average of SG 1057; malic 1.07%; tannin 0.20%

Cider: Very dry sharp with a characteristic flavour. Very useful for blending.

GENNET MOYLE
Dual Purpose Apple

In Hogg's Fruit Manual of 1884 he writes of Worlidge's opinion of Gennet Moyle , 'a pleasant and necessary fruit in the kitchen and one of the best cider apples.' The trees are said to be 'great bearers'. Gennet Moyle, meaning literally mule or hybrid scion, was used in his time as a stock for grafting with choice varieties. It is a true pitcher that should root easily from cuttings or branches with a bur-knot, and was therefore useful for propagating in quantity for rootstocks. It is an ancient apple which is still propagated for collectors, but there is some uncertainty about the true identity of the present source of mother trees.

The large green, rounded, rather flattened fruits are ready mid October.

Fruits: Large, 55–>60mm. Oblate or flattened conical with a rounded base.; somewhat ribbed, often lopsided. Short stem usually within the deep, narrow cavity or projecting slightly [5–8mm]. Eye basin small, narrow, slightly crowned. Skin smooth, pale green ripening to yellow-green. Usually flushed rather brownish pink on the sunny side. Flesh juicy, melting, greenish and quite sharp.

Cider: Hogg goes on to quote 'It makes and incomparable pleasant liquor, but a little weakish, and fit only to be drunk by ladies in the summer, and will not keep so long as the more masculine cyders . . .' If the cultivar in current use is the true Gennet Moyle it should live up to this praise.

GIN

Early Sharp Cider Apple

Synonym: Gatcombe

The apples shown at the Bath and West Exhibition in 1893 were noted to come from Butleigh, and Gin is still fairly frequently found in the area around Glastonbury. It picked up its synonym Gatcombe when it was sent in to the Cider Institute for cider making trials in 1910 as an unknown cider apple from Gatcombe Farm, Long Ashton. It was then distributed over the other counties in the earliest trial orchards planted pre 1920. Mature trees are medium sized, compact with a dense, round head. Crops are regular and heavy. Young bush trees tend to be upright, spreading and open. It flowers late in May.

Gin apples are conical, yellow with a large, ribbed eye and sometimes a brilliant patch of flush. It matures and drops early in October but because the skin is rather delicate, the fruit does not keep well on the ground.

Fruit: Medium, but can be fairy large, 45–60mm. Flattened conical, sometimes tending to cylindrical with a broad nose and narrow rounded base; ribbed and often irregular. Stem woody, sometimes strigged, within or projecting slightly from a small, tight cavity; stem cavity absent in off-year king fruits. Eye basin medium, well defined, often slightly puckered or crowned, distinctly ribbed; calyx open, sepals upright, short, green at base. Skin pale soft yellow; smooth, slightly waxy; scab susceptible; russet usually slight but occasionally heavy in the stem cavity and spreading in a network over cheek; lenticels small green or red dots. Flush occasionally present, usually less than one third; thin orange or pink. Flesh mild sharp with some mild astringency, clear fresh flavour; white or greenish-white, melting texture.

Juice: SG 1060; acidity 0.20%; tannin 0.22%

Cider: Very pleasant sweet, full bodied, with medium acidity. Flavour and aroma fruity and good. Fermentation slow to medium. Gin cider is very useful alone or blended.

GLASS APPLE

Dual Purpose Apple

Synonyms: Snell's Glass Apple, Snell's White

Raised by Mr Snell a market gardener of Radland Mill, St Dominick in the Taymar Valley, an area where it is quite often found. It has been known since 1934 , but records are scant and it may be older than this. The trees are quite vigorous and said to be scab free.

The large pale gold apples are ripe by early September.

Fruits: Medium to large, 55–occasionally >60mm. Conical, flattened; regular in section. Stem very short or a stout stub [1–7mm] within a small, shallow, gold russeted cavity. Eye open in a broad, shallow, fairly smooth basin. Skin yellow-green ripening to greenish-yellow. Lenticels show as small green dots. Flush absent. Flesh sub-acid, juicy, melting, yellowish.

Cider: Unlikely to contribute much to cidermaking.

GOLDEN BALL

Late Maturing Medium Sharp Cider Apple

Synonyms: in Dorset: Polly, Go Boyn, also Neverblight

Many samples of fruit came to the Cider Institute during 1926–33, mostly from the Netherbury, Stoke Abbott area of Dorset. It is a variety that dates back beyond the RHS Exhibition of 1883 and is still occasionally found as single trees in old orchards in West Dorset. It has recently been redistributed through the DATA Project [2011]. It is a first rate sharp variety that must always have made a useful contribution to the character of Dorset cider.

It seems to be a robust, scab-free variety that grows well, making a medium sized tree, upright then spreading with crop. Cropping is heavy but biennial. Flowering late in mid May. Leaves small, ovate with a crenate margin.

The small conical russeted apples are hard, deceptively green-brown at first, ripening to a golden yellow with a little pinkish flush by mid October-early November.

Fruit: Medium smallish; 40–55mm occasionally >55mm. Conical, flat nose; rounded and regular with a trace of soft rounded ribs. Stem thick and fleshy, within or projecting slightly from a small, narrow cavity. Eye basin small, slightly bumpy, tending to crowned. Sepals short and closed. Skin dry. Russet dots, patches and often a fine network spreading across cheek. Colour yellow-green ripening to golden yellow. Usually a little diffuse orange or pinkish, more noticeable in immature fruit which is deceptively reddish-brown. Flesh yellowish, chewy, mild sharp

Juice: Medium sharp. Sugar content often below average.
SG 1045; acidity 0.55%; tannin 0.15%

Cider: Fermentation moderate. Cider, body fair, medium brisk. Can be poor. But the prize winning cider from Stoke Abbott in 1928 was described as; *'A very useful cider, clean, brisk with a pleasant flavour.'*

GOLDEN BITTERSWEET
Midseason Mild Bittersweet Cider Apple

Synonym: Best Bearer

This apple was described by Hogg in 1886 as *'A good Devonshire cider apple which bears well and keeps without wasting. This was sent me by Mr Rendall of Netherton Manor, Devon.'* It is a variety that seems long-lived and often crops up as single trees in fields, farms and orchards in West Dorset. It is a good bittersweet if well grown and has recently been redistributed with the DATA Project [2011]. It is also kept in the National Fruit Collection, Brogdale. Golden Bittersweet trees are vigorous with upright branches and much bare wood. It is rather slow to come into full bearing but it seems to be fairly trouble free. Flowering mid season

The apples are large, lightly crowned and pale greenish yellow with conspicuous russet dots. Ready early-mid October, but keep well.

Fruit: Medium-large; 45–60mm. Flattened conical, broad rounded base and flat nose; broadly ribbed, angular, indistinctly crowned. Stem short and stubby, occasionally projecting slightly from a narrow, often heavily gold russeted cavity. Eye basin small, tight, puckered, sometimes with 5–10 low crowns. Sepals open, variable, sometimes closed, upright, green. Skin dry. Lenticels conspicuous as small russet, green or red dots. Russet mostly around the eye but often heavy golden streaks in the stem cavity, sometimes spreading as a light network over the cheek. Colour pale green ripening to pale golden yellow. Often a trace of pale orange flush. Flesh chewy, sweet with some mild bitterness.

Juice: SG 1059; acidity 0.21%; tannin 0.49%

Cider: Mild bittersweet

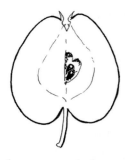

GOLLY KNAPP

Late Bittersweet Cider Apple

An unknown cider apple was brought to Powerstock Pressing Day 2007 from Punknowle, Nr Bridport, West Dorset, the only remaining tree of its sort in a very dilapidated old orchard. We gave it the same name as the house beside the orchard. In spite of the age and poor condition of the tree, a sample of fruit made some very nice bittersweet cider. Trees have recently been propagated and distributed through the DATA Project [2013]. This variety is a find that may have considerable potential but it remains to be seen how these trees will perform on a dwarfing rootstock.

Golly Knapp apples are smallish, conical and russeted green with a touch of orange flush. Ready late October to early November.

Fruit: Medium, 45–55mm. Conical, sometimes slightly waisted and cylindrical; more or less rounded in section. Stem quite long [10–14mm], woody and projecting distinctly from a narrow, deep, well russeted cavity. Eye wide open in a shallow, moderately crowned basin, sepals reflexed, green. Skin rough but waxy. Russet often heavy and spreading as a network over half the fruit. Colour pale green, always with a patch of diffuse brownish-orange flush. Flesh mild bittersweet, chewy cider apple texture. Core small and tightly packed with seeds.

Juice: SG 1060; acidity 0.21%; tannin 0.39%; sugar 15.0%

Cider: High sugar content suggests a high potential alcohol! Should make a good cider on its own or blended with a bittersweet.

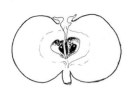

HALSTOW NATURAL

Mid-season Sweet Cider Apple

Trees of this typical Devon sweet cider variety are sometimes still found in the Tedburn St Mary area of Devon near Halstow village where it originated. Its trees are large and spreading. Said to be scab resistant. Flowers early to mid May.

The 'codlin' type apples are sweet and low in acid, pale yellow and rounded. Ready in October.

Fruit: Medium to large, 50–60mm. Flattened round with a broad nose and base. Rounded ribs especially around the nose. Stem usually a stub in a deep russeted cavity. Eye basin broad and quite deep, slightly furrowed with small rounded crowns. Sepals green, reflexed. Eye more or less closed. Skin pale primrose yellow, smooth and waxy. Lenticels show as large dots sometimes russeted. Flesh pure sweet; white.

Cider: Unfortunately there are no notes.

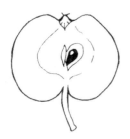

HANGDOWN

Late Mid Season Mild Bittersweet Cider Apple

Synonyms: Horners, Hangydown, Pocket Apple [in Devon]

A Hangdown tree is easily identified by its habit. It is compact, usually fairly small sized, with many twiggy branches which droop when heavy with fruit. It is widely distributed throughout Somerset and South Devon, where it is often called Pocket Apple. It also occurs in a few old trials orchards in other counties but is no longer in favour because of the small size of its fruit. There are several closely related varieties going under the name of Hangdown, all with the same drooping habit and similar fruit of varying quality. Many of them are seedlings or so-called, Improved Hangdowns. The true Hangdown is said to have originated in the Glastonbury area where it still occurs quite frequently. Hangdown crops well and regularly on light soils but lacks vigour on heavy land. It is quite scab susceptible and flowers rather late in May.

The small green fruits which usually hang in clusters, are round with long, thin stems. The cores are tightly stuffed full of seeds. They are usually ready to drop by late October.

Fruit: Small, less than 40–45mm. Rounded or slightly cylindrical with a narrow rounded base. Stem thin and woody, sometimes swelling slightly at the junction with the fruit, projecting distinctly or considerably from a small, narrow, deep cavity. Eye basin medium, large for the size of the fruit, deep, usually puckered and slightly beaded, ribbed; calyx closed or slightly open, sepals touching, reflexed at the tips, sometimes green at the base. Skin yellow or greenish-yellow; smooth and slightly waxy; russet usually confined to stem cavity, sometimes streaky or a network over part of the cheek; lenticels usually inconspicuous but sometimes large and corky or red on the flush. Usually there is a patch of thin red or pinkish-orange flush on the cheeks, often less than 30%, rarely up to 60%. Flesh sweet and usually slightly astringent; yellowish-white; very soft.

Juice: SG 1056; acidity 0.20%; tannin 0.28%

Cider: Hangdown is only mildly bittersweet and makes average quality cider.

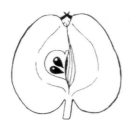

HARRY MASTERS JERSEY

Late Mid-season Bittersweet Cider Apple

Synonym: Sometimes also called Port Wine

Harry Masters, nurseryman of Woolston, Somerset raised this variety and Yarlington Mill, probably seedlings with the same parentage. Both are typical Somerset 'jersey' apples in shape and astringency. Both immediately enjoyed great popularity in the late 19th century and have since been widely planted with great success in modern bush cider orchards. Harry Masters Jersey was included in the earliest trial orchards planted before 1920. A Harry Masters tree is medium sized with a compact head. The bark of young wood has distinct lenticels which make it easy to distinguish from other varieties during the dormant season. As a bush tree its crops are not heavy but are fairly regular. Crops from traditional orchards are biennial but good. Harry Masters flowers late mid-season just before Chisel Jersey, but its blossom usually overlaps sufficiently to make it a good pollinator for that variety. Before young bush trees settle into regular cropping, the fruit is often very large and can be prone to water core.

Harry Masters Jersey is typical conical jersey shape, flushed dark red and coated with a fine, distinctive bluish, waxy bloom. It is quite a late apple, ready late October to early November.

Fruit: Medium, often large on young trees, 45–55mm. Conical with a flattened base and a pointed nose tending to a snout. Stem projecting slightly but often level with the base; cavity medium. Eye basin smallish, shallow, puckered, often ribbed; calyx usually closed or slightly open, sepals touching, short, green at base. Skin greenish-yellow; smooth, covered when ripe with a bluish, waxy bloom; russet confined to stem cavity or spreading slightly; lenticels often conspicuous, large, corky, surrounded by patch of russet. Flush more than 65%, diffuse, flecked and slightly striped dark red. Flesh sweet and astringent; white, sometimes reddened below skin; hard and dry.

Juice: SG 1056; acidity 0.20%; tannin 0.32%

Cider: Medium to full bittersweet, Harry Masters Jersey has soft astringent tannin and makes a very good quality cider.

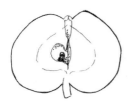

HOCKINGS GREEN

Mid-season Dual Purpose Apple

Raised at Illand Farm, Coads Green, Callington, this was once a popular apple and it is still quite common in Cornish orchards. There are many trees of Hockings Green growing in the area north of Exeter and it can often be found in west Devon. It is not technically a cider apple, although frequently used as such, but cooks well in October to November and passes for a dessert later when the sharpness has mellowed. The trees are moderately vigorous and form a rounded head. Hockings Green is said to be very hardy and enjoy wet and windy conditions. It can be slightly scab susceptible but it does seem very resistant to canker. Flowers in the first two weeks in May

Hockings Green is a large, rather angular and flattened green apple that ripens to lime green in warm dry years. Ready by mid October.

Fruit: Large usually 60mm or more. Cylindrical or flattened conical with a flat nose and broad base. Rather angular with distinct ribs, often slightly lopsided. Stem a stub or just showing [<10mm] from a narrow, quite deep cavity. Eye usually closed or slightly open in a fairly narrow and shallow, much crowned and ribbed basin. Tube often open to the core. Skin mid green ripening to yellow green, sometimes half covered with a diffuse orange flush or occasional red flecks and prominent green lenticels. Flesh greenish, juicy and melting .

Juice: The taste is rather culinary and full sharp.

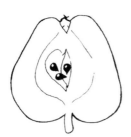

IMPROVED DOVE

Mid Season Bittersweet Cider Apple

This is one of the many 'improvements' on the popular Somerset variety Dove or Pennard Dove. Although having excellent vintage qualities, the true Dove lost its resistance to scab, was predisposed to virus infection and consequently fell out of favour. Improved Dove, Stone Dove, Dove Seedling, Late Dove and others, are more recent introductions, probably all seedlings of the true Dove that came from the Glastonbury area in the early part of the last century. Improved Dove was originally resistant to scab and is the only one to have survived in significant numbers in Somerset.

Improved Dove quickly makes a strong tree, upright but spreading with crop and with a good, dominant centre leader. Although lateral branches are a bit sparse in young trees, spurring is free. It is a partial tip bearer, so cropping is regular at first but often becomes biennial. This variety may also have become prone to scab by now, but perhaps not so much as the original Dove. It flowers late, from mid May to the end of the month.

The fruit is tall, broadly conical, yellow striped and very similar to Dove itself but usually larger. Maturing mid October to early November.

Fruit: Medium, 45–55mm. Conical, elongated sometimes with a nose; fairly regular or slightly elliptical in section. Stem woody or sometimes fleshy, level with base or projecting slightly from a small, conical cavity, stem cavity often appearing deeper in section. Eye basin small, slightly puckered and ribbed tending to shoulders; calyx tightly closed, sepals fairly long and overlapping. Skin green or yellow green; smooth, waxy; scab susceptible; russet confined to stem cavity, rarely spreading over cheek; lenticels usually inconspicuous, sometimes with a light surround. Flush usually 30–70% lightly flecked and striped, dark red, over brownish-orange diffuse. Flesh mild bittersweet; soft, juicy; greenish white, browning rapidly.

Juice: SG 1050; acidity 0.17%; tannin 0.38%

Cider: No cider-maker's notes found. Likely to be a useful bittersweet for blending.

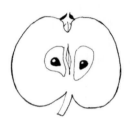

IMPROVED HANGDOWN

Mid Season Mild Bittersweet Cider Apple

Synonyms: Improved Horners, Osier

Most records of fruit sent to Long Ashton came from the Glastonbury to Wedmore area in the early 1900s, when the variety was first recorded as Improved Hangdown or Horners. It was exhibited at the RHS show in 1934 but has never been widely propagated. It was collected from the Whetton's Museum orchard in 1974 and subsequently sent to the National Fruit Trials collection at Brogdale, by then named Osier. The trees are rather weak and weeping like the true Hangdown. It may well be a seedling from it. Flowering time is mid May. Fruit is ready for harvesting by the end of October.

The apples are pale green with a trace of pink on the sunny side, topped by a crowned eye basin with distinctive broad, green and leafy sepals.

Fruit: Medium to large, 45–60mm. Cylindrical, broad nose and base; rounded tending to ribbed. Stem long, thin, woody, projecting slightly or distinctly from a medium, deep cavity; stem short, cavity slight in king fruit. Eye basin medium, narrow, deep, crowned and furrowed, sometimes beaded; sepals partially open, long, green and leafy. Skin pale yellow-green; smooth, dry becoming waxy; scab susceptible; lenticels sometimes small red dots on flush only. Flush frequently a trace to 30% on the sunny side, pink or brownish orange diffuse. Flesh sweet with mild astringency; pleasant flavour, chewy, greenish.

Juice: SG 1056; acidity 0.23%; tannin 0.24%

Cider: No cider-maker's notes found. Improved Hangdown juice is mildly bittersweet and flavourable so should make a fair cider when blended with something of character.

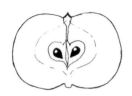

IMPROVED KINGSTON BLACK

Late Sharp Cider Apple

Synonym: Sometimes also incorrectly Port Wine

Although the name would presume this variety to be even better than the legendary Kingston Black, this is unfortunately completely untrue. It is relatively disease free, certainly a major improvement, but Improved Kingston Black is a sharp, lacking in tannin, which makes an indifferent cider only. It is definitely not to be confused with the balanced bittersharp qualities of the true Kingston Black. It is more likely to be related to Black Vallis, a very similar apple. First records at Long Ashton are from fruit sent in by Squire Neville Grenville of Butleigh Court in 1908, after which it was planted in several trial orchards. It has been described as 'a good sort', and was regarded as one of the best 'all rounders' by those who grew it at the time. It still crops up in orchards around Butleigh, and at Glastonbury, Baltonsborough, West Bradley and elsewhere. Mature trees can be quite large and spreading. They carry a full head of leaves, dark and free of disease. It certainly crops better and is less disease susceptible than Kingston Black proper. It flowers in early May.

The fruits which mature in late October, are a similar size and shape to Kingston Black, rather flattened. They are also almost completely covered in a dark red flush which is never so dense, or so black, but more cherry red.

Fruit: Medium to large, 55–more than 60mm. Cylindrical or flattened conical almost oblate, broad nose and base; tending to ribbed. Stem absent or a thick fleshy stub; cavity small, narrow, absent in king fruit. Eye basin small, narrow, usually smooth but tending to crowned, occasionally beaded; sepals short, broad. Skin pale yellow, dry or slightly waxy. Flush always present, virtually complete, strong bright red or pink, to dark red, faintly striped; skin colour showing only in stem cavity. Flesh sharp; hard, melting dessert texture, white, vascular strands red, reddened under skin.

Juice: Sharp, variable acidity. SG 1056; acidity 0.30–80%; tannin 0.15%

Cider: A mild sharp cider with a rather insipid flavour.

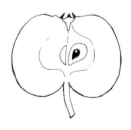

IMPROVED LAMBROOK PIPPIN

Early Mild Sharp Cider Apple

The original Lambrook Pippin makes excellent cider but its fruits are rather small. The Improved version was most likely also raised in Martock, Somerset, either at Symes' or Porter's nursery and may have started out as an eating apple.

It has larger fruit but the juice is mild sharp, often with a good sugar content but lacking in astringency. It was introduced for Taunton Cider in the '60s and appears as bush trees in many orchards planted for them in Somerset the last half of the century, but is by no means common. This noticeably early flowering variety is often in full bloom at the end of April. It is sometimes easily spotted in a bush orchard by the brush of suckers which sprout around the base of each tree. It is vigorous and spreading, the stronger branches carrying some bare wood.

The fruit is large and attractive, with yellow skin and bright red stripes, a long stalk and prominent lenticels. It is a useful, early maturing variety which is ready by the end of September or early October. Unfortunately it is thin skinned and rather prone to codling moth attack so easily rots if left too long on the ground.

Fruit: Large, 55–more than 60mm. Round or flattened cylindrical; slightly angular. Stem long, green-yellow, woody, projecting distinctly from a large, deep and steep cavity. Eye basin absent or very slight, slightly bumpy or beaded; calyx open, sepals upright in a free crown. Skin pale primrose yellow; smooth, rather greasy; russet occasionally in cavities; lenticels very conspicuous as dots or with a pale surround on the flush. Always, from 20–75%, carmine flecks and stripes over diffuse orange flush. Flesh dessert character, low acid and sweet; yellowish, sometimes red under the skin, melting or crisp texture.

Juice: SG 1067; acidity 0.50%; tannin 0.08%

Cider: No cider-maker's comments found.

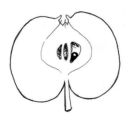

IRONSIDES

Very Late Dual Purpose Apple

Synonyms: May have many alternative names; possibly Iron Pin, Ironstone Pippin or even French Crab. Also possibly Leatherjacket, but this is described as bittersweet

Clearly a very old variety, perhaps even 16th century. Hogg refers to this Ironsides in his Fruit Manual of 1884 as *'A cooking apple which keeps in good condition to January-February. It appears to be a Dorsetshire apple, sent to me by Mr C T Hall of Osmington Lodge, Weymouth.'* It was still often found in West Dorset orchards when Pickford made his survey in the 1930s but now only occurs infrequently as single, aged trees. It is probably of little value for cider making, its greatest quality might be its long-keeping. Trees have recently been propagated and distributed through the DATA Project [2013]. Growth is strong and vigorous. Flowering mid-season.

It makes a medium sized, rounded, often rather scabby green apple with a few red stripes. And as Hogg reported, it matures by late November but is hard enough to keep indefinitely!

Fruit: Small-medium, 45–55mm. Round or flattened conical with a rounded nose and base; softly ribbed. Stem variable [3–10mm], within the small, narrow cavity or projecting slightly. Usually woody but sometimes green and fleshy if long. Eye basin small, shallow, rather bumpy or irregularly crowned into the ribs, occasionally with a trace of beading. Sepals open, upright and free. Skin smooth and slightly waxy, occasionally with some russet. Colour dark green ripening to grass-green, frequently a trace of lightly speckled brownish-orange on the sunny side or on the nose. Flesh rather non-descript sharp, hard and chewy, greenish, browning quickly around the core. Core variable but often tightly filled with seeds: tube is a broad cone.

Juice: Deep straw colour. Rather non-descript flavour.
SG 1053, acidity 0.77%; tannin 0.22%

Cider: Described at the Cider Institute as '*mediocre*'. But this variety's late maturity and keeping quality could be useful.

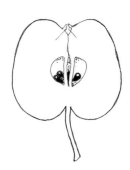

KATY

Sub-acid Dessert Apple

Synonym: Katja

This variety is likely to be found only as relatively young trees since it has fairly recently earned much popularity as a heavy cropping, early maturing juice apple. It originated in Sweden, a cross between James Grieve and Worcester Pearmain, where it is grown as an eating apple under the name Katja.

It was renamed Katy when it was introduced into the UK by Long Ashton in 1968. Katy trees have an ungainly habit, throwing strong growth with much bare wood in the early years. They are very prolific and inclined to set heavily but, if they are not allowed to over-crop for the first few harvests, they will settle down into good middle age productivity.

Katy is ready to start the pressing season in early September. The large bright red waxy, glossy fruit are very attractive to birds so need to be harvested promptly since they rot quickly, especially if already damaged.

Fruit: Large to very large, 55–>60mm. Tall conical cylindrical with a broad flat nose and a rounded base; tending to ribbed in section. Stem long slender

[25–30mm] projects considerably from a deep cavity usually lined with greenish russet. Eye basin medium size, fairly smooth or slightly furrowed. Eye open, sepals green and free. Always almost covered with a bright red flush with darker flecks and a pale yellow patch around the nose. Lenticels sometimes conspicuous small brown dots. Flesh yellowish, juicy and melting.

Juice: Very sweet and sub-acid.

Cider: Often used as a single varietal cider with good light colour and refreshing mild flavour.

KILLERTON SHARP

Early Mid-season Mild Sharp Cider Apple

The original tree is in the old orchard of the Killerton Estate, belonging to the National Trust. It was one of two trees, propagated and named by Veitch's nursery of Exeter in the 1950s. There is a single tree in the Long Ashton trial orchard at Christon Court, marked incorrectly as Killerton Sweet. It was recently propagated mainly as standard trees and currently on nursery lists as Killerton Sharp. The following description was made from fruit from the original tree and from a newly propagated tree in the Ranger's yard at Killerton. Trees are large, open and erect. Cropping and growth are good. [The original tree although protected from the public, is no longer erect but has fallen on its side. It still produces a few fruit every year]. Flowers mid-season.

Killerton Sharp apples are rather large, flat-rounded, greenish-yellow flushed red. Ready early October.

Fruit: Large, 55–>60mm. Flattened conical with a broad base, king fruits often cylindrical. Often lopsided and angular with well rounded ribs. Stem often off-set, with a bulge at the base, usually projecting slightly or distinctly [5–12mm] from a shallow cavity filled with golden russet. Eye basin slight and shallow, rather irregular, slightly bumpy, sometimes beaded. Eye slightly open. Skin pale primrose yellow, dry, smooth or roughened by a network of ochre russet on the cheeks. Lenticels brown dots or large, russeted, sometimes pink. Sometimes up to 1/3 flushed slight light red flecks over an orange blush. Flesh chewy, yellowish. Taste rather non-descript.

Juice: SG 1050; acidity 1.00%; tannin 0.10%

Cider: Said to yield a soft pleasant cider. Sugar content is often low and fermentation rather above average

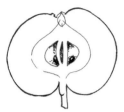

KILLERTON SWEET

Mid-season Mild Bittersweet Cider Apple

The original tree grows side by side with the Killerton Sharp tree in the old orchard of the National Trust Killerton Estate where both were named by Veitch in the 1950s. It was listed by Prof Barker from his trials at the Cider Institute in 1937 as a Devon sweet cider apple but there may have been some confusion as to which tree was which. Most trees currently on nursery lists are Killerton Sharp. Killerton Sweet certainly produces better flavoured apples with greater promise for good cider. This description is made recently from the original tree and fruit from a newly propagated tree in Ranger's yard at Killerton. Tree are large, open and erect when mature. Cropping and growth is good. Scab susceptible. Flowers mid-season.

Killerton Sweet apples are rather flattened or oblate and more than half covered with a crimson flush. Ready mid October.

Fruit: Medium, 45–55mm. Flattened conical to oblate, with broad rounded nose and small base, ribbed from the eye basin, slightly angular in section. Stem thick, often with a bulge at the base, projecting slightly from a small, russeted cavity. Eye basin slight, rather irregularly crowned and beaded. Eye closed. Skin yellow to yellow-green. Slight streaky network of russet. Nearly always more than half covered with a strong crimson flush, flecked, speckled and slightly striped. Flesh mild bittersweet, chewy, yellowish, occasionally red around the eye.

Juice: SG 1060; acidity 0.73%; tannin 0.23%

Cider: No Long Ashton notes.

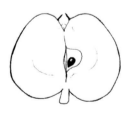

KINGS FAVOURITE

Late Mid-Season Sharp Cider Apple

Synonyms: Crimson King generally but Kings Favourite in Dorset. Also less often John Toucher's; Jackson's. Incorrectly Brimley Red

This is a familiar variety in West Dorset where it is known only as Kings Favourite. It was said to have been propagated by Mr John Toucher of Bewley Down, Chardstock on the borders of Dorset and Devon hence its synonyms, but was later named Crimson King when it was adopted by the nursery trade. It still occurs as mature trees in western Somerset and adjacent parts of Devon and Dorset. It was sometimes used as a replacement for gaps in old orchards, but it has not been chosen recently for use in bush orchards because of its vigour.

It is a strong triploid variety that makes a large, spreading tree with many bare branches without spurs when young, but it is reputed to crop generously and fairly annually as it matures. Trees also seems to be long lived. It flowers mid season but is a poor pollinator.

The apples resemble coloured Bramleys, from which they are distinguished by their bright crimson, striped flush and deep, open eye. They also mature much later than Bramley, not being ready until November.

Fruit: Medium or large, 55–more than 60mm. Variable, usually conical, rarely cylindrical, round or oblate; irregular. Stem stout, fleshy or woody, rarely bulging at junction with fruit or spur, projecting very slightly or level with the base; stem cavity variable, small but can be deep or shallow. Eye basin fairly wide, usually deep, often irregular and slightly ribbed; calyx open, sepals long if not broken, reflexed and free. Skin greenish-yellow; smooth, slightly waxy; russet usual, spreading over cheek, usually in streaks, often rough and scaly in stem cavity. Scab susceptible. Flush usually 30–65%, mainly diffuse, with some crimson flecking and striping. Flesh sharp with no astringency; white or greenish, sometimes reddened below skin.

Juice: SG 1044; acidity 0.60%; tannin 0.13%

Cider: In a good year this variety's cider can be good alone without blending. It is medium sharp, light and fruity and usually of above average quality. Fermentation can be rather rapid and the sugar content is often low.

KINGSTON BITTER

Late Bittersweet Cider Apple

Found in the south and west of Devon and probably hailing from the South Hams, Kingston Bitter was propagated by Hills nursery near Totnes who sent it to the Bath & West in 1896. It was also listed in the RHS Exhibition of 1934 and described in the MAFF leaflet No. 104, as 'A variety of repute in some districts of Devon, but further trial over a wider area is necessary before its merits can be assessed satisfactorily.' Trees are moderately vigorous, large, upright and prolific. Cropping is good but can be biennial. Said to be scab resistant. Flowers late mid-season, towards late May. This is a variety with a good pedigree coming from an area with a tradition for making excellent cider. It deserves to be planted more widely.

Kingston Bitter apples are rather rounded, with a long stem and almost covered in a dark striped red flush. Ready late October.

Fruit: Medium, 45–55mm. Rounded conical with a round base and flat nose. Rounded and regular in section. Stem long thin, woody, projecting distinctly from a fairly deep cavity. Eye basin small, smooth, narrow and shallow. Eye more or less open, sepals upright. Skin shiny, smooth, yellow-green. More or less completely covered in a bright red flush with short, dark red stripes.

Juice: Few records were made but sugar was reputed to be above average. 1994 sample SG1068; acidity 0.29%; tannin 0.34%

Cider: Has a good reputation but sadly no Long Ashton notes.

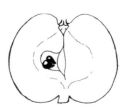

KINGSTON BLACK

Late Mid-season Bittersharp Cider Apple

Synonym: Black Taunton, now dropped in favour of Kingston Black

Kingston Black, thought to be named after the village of Kingston, near Taunton, is probably related to other Somerset bittersharps varieties such as Cap of Liberty, Lambrook Pippin and Porters Perfection. It reached almost legendary status in the late 20th century as a vintage cider apple, although to many, this fame is somewhat exaggerated. Kingston Black juice is bittersharp with well balanced tannin and acidity. Fruit from old standard trees is often high in sugar and will make a full bodied, single variety cider with a distinctive flavour. Because of its popularity it was widely planted throughout all the cider growing regions, but its performance varies considerably depending on soil types and location. Scott's Catalogue in 1873, listed it as *'A handsome grower and a great bearer . . . It is to be found in almost every orchard in this neighbourhood'* [mid Somerset]. Recent bush orchard plantings have been rather disappointing and have not achieved quite the same vintage quality. However, it is still planted in limited quantities for the specialist market of Kingston Black cider.

The variety has many faults as an orchard tree; it is over-vigorous, a shy cropper, has poor, malformed, almost stemless flowers overlooked by pollinating insects, and tends to be very susceptible to scab and canker. The mature tree has a thin, open, spreading head formed of long, unbranched limbs. The final size of the tree depends on the incidence of scab and canker.

The shape of the fruit can be quite variable. It is flushed very dark red, sometimes almost black, and has a rich fruity flavour. It matures quite late, in early November.

Fruit: Medium to small, 45–55mm. Variable shape; basically conical or flattened, tending to cylindrical. Stem variable, medium thick, thick fleshy stems common;

within the cavity or level with the base; cavity rather narrow and shallow but sometimes deep. Eye well defined shallow or deep and steep sided, sometimes slightly puckered; calyx slightly open, sepals free. Skin yellow-green; dry, rather rough; russet spreading slightly to the cheek, sometimes forming a network, usually scaly in the stem cavity; lenticels conspicuous, large, irregular, often surrounded by a light area. Flush always more than 75%, often complete, flecked or slightly striped very dark red, almost black. Flesh bittersharp, mildly acidic with some astringency which is often not marked, rich fruity almost dessert flavour; reddened, sometimes white; dry, floury.

Juice: SG 1061; acidity 0.58%; tannin 0.19%

Cider: Kingston Black's juice is bittersharp with well balanced tannin and acidity which will make a full bodied, single variety cider with a distinctive flavour. The results from fruit from young trees may be disappointing, since, like all varieties, its vintage qualities improve with maturity.

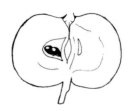

LAMBROOK PIPPIN

Late Mid-season Bittersharp Cider Apple

This variety was first recorded at the Bath and West Show in 1895, from a sample of fruit sent in from Martock described as a very useful late cider apple. Lambrook Pippin is related to Porters Perfection, Kingston Black and Cap of Liberty and naturally makes cider of excellent quality; bittersharp with superior flavour and aroma. It originated in Somerset, possibly either from Symes of Martock or Porter's nursery in Lambrook. It was frequently used as a stem builder and mainframe in orchards in that part of the county. Its strong vigorous growth often outgrew the top-worked variety and trees, part Lambrook Pippin, part another weaker variety, are quite common in old orchards. On its own it forms a fair sized tree, strong and with dense, vigorous growth. It is renowned for its remarkable powers of regeneration. It is slow to come into cropping and biennial but crops well when bearing. It flowers mid to late May.

The fruit, which matures in November, is medium sized, flattened and rounded, flushed pinkish-orange with red flecks and conspicuous lenticels. The eye is often a distinctive feature, wide open with prominent reflexed sepals. Lambrook Pippin fruit will sometimes twin like its offspring Porter's Perfection.

Fruit: Small to medium, 40–55mm. Oblate flattened rounded, base rounded; sometimes irregular with scab; twinning occasionally. Stem level with base or projecting distinctly, usually fairly thick, fleshy, sometimes with a strig; stem cavity fairly small and shallow. Eye basin small, shallow, sometimes slightly puckered and ribbed; calyx open, sepals fairly long, often free, and reflexed at tips. Skin yellowish green; smooth, slightly waxy; very scab susceptible; lenticels usually small but conspicuous, surrounded by a light area, sometimes corky. Flush about 60%, pinkish-orange heavily flecked with red, sometimes slightly striped. Flesh sharp with some tannin; greenish white, woolly, juicy and hard.

Juice: SG 1055; acidity 0.58%; tannin 0.24%

Cider: Lambrook Pippin makes a nice light cider of excellent quality, flavour and superior aroma. Fermentation is usually slow.

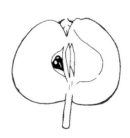

LANGWORTHY

Late Sharp Cider Apple

Synonyms: Wyatt's Seedling or Sweet [in Somerset], Sour Natural [in Devon]

Langworthy is usually recorded as a Devon apple for this is its usual name in that county, but Langworthy and Wyatt's Seedling are undoubtedly one and the same. Mr Wyatt from Kingweston in south Somerset often sent this variety in for cider making competitions at the Cider Institute in the 1930s, sometimes naming it Wyatt's Sweet in spite of its sharp taste. It was also called Wyatt's Seedling in Newton St Cyres in Devon where it grew in several orchards, but towards the end of the 1930s, fruit from this locality was consistently called Langworthy. In the 1932 Cider Competition at Long Ashton, Langworthy won first prize as a mild sharp. Afterwards enjoying some popularity, it was widely planted from Exeter to Crediton, Taunton to Sutton Montis, and at Whiteways own orchard in Whimple, Devon. It is not so popular nowadays in bush orchards, mostly because of it small sized fruits. This variety is reputed to be a good cropper but rather mildew susceptible. Growth may be slow in early years but mature trees are large and spreading. It flowers in early May.

The small, neat rounded, deep red russeted fruits with tiny stem and eye basins, are not ready until early November. They are flushed bright red and covered with a distinctive patterned russet and dots.

Fruit: Very variable, usually medium but often small, less than 40–55mm. Rounded or flattened conical, sometimes with a nose, base broad; regular. Stem usually fairly stout but can be long and thin; stem cavity small, often almost absent. Eye basin slight, puckered, lightly ribbed, sometimes a trace of beading; calyx open, sepals free, short, upright, often broken. Skin light greenish-yellow; smooth, slightly waxy; no scab; russet a distinguishing feature, golden, often heavily dotted all over, associated with lenticels. Flush more than 60%; bright red, flecked and slightly striped dark maroon. Flesh mild sharp sometimes with some astringency; crisp, white.

Juice: SG 1051; acidity 0.47%; tannin 0.12%

Cider: Langworthy makes a pleasant, brisk, light, sweet cider with a good flavour and aroma, but rather body deficient. Very useful alone or blended.

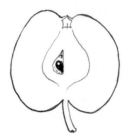

LATE GOLD

Full Bittersweet Cider Apple

This new cider apple was raised by a talented amateur wine and cider maker from Suffolk, the late Alan Rowe in about 2000. It is a cross between full bittersweet Medaille d'Or and Yarlington Mill. Late Gold inherits the best qualities of Yarlington; its easy-going forbearance with less than ideal orchard conditions, its tolerance to disease and its good fruit size. Medaille d'Or gives it superior vintage quality but carries with it heavy bitter tannin. Late Gold trees are moderately vigorous, reasonably regular cropping but flower late, towards the end of May. It could prove a very useful and robust late maturing variety. Young trees are just becoming available from the nursery ready for distribution.

The butter yellow conical apples with a distinctively long stem are ready early to mid November.

Fruit: Medium sized, 45–55mm. Conical with a broad flat nose. Stem long and projecting considerably from a slightly russeted cavity. Eye basin deep, rather irregularly crowned and lightly russeted. Eye tightly closed with short green sepals. Skin is smooth, dry and overall a butter yellow with no flush. Flesh is yellowish, chewy and good bittersweet. Young trees are not yet cropping but this new apple variety is likely to be very useful for blending with late sharp varieties.

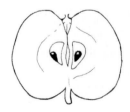

LE BRET

Mid Season Sweet Cider Apple

Le Bret was named after Mrs Le Bret of Bristol who brought some apples to Long Ashton in 1956. It proved to be an interesting sweet cider apple and was included in the orchard trials in the 1950s. Le Bret was widely planted in both the South West and in Hereford in the 1970s, perhaps more by mistake than by intent. Some were planted under the name Sweet Alford, a variety which it only superficially resembles. This was most probably a simple mistake made during the propagation of trees for new bush orchards at the time, but it is still referred to as Sweet Alford in many orchards. Le Bret is moderately vigorous and makes a medium to large tree with a dense spreading head. It flowers very early in late April. It is easy to train as a bush tree with a strong, dominant centre leader, but spurring is only moderate.

Le Bret is ready by mid to late October. Its apples are large and bold, yellow flushed with bright scarlet, and have distinctly upright sepals. Sweet Alford fruits are usually smaller, less bright and have a much longer stalk.

Fruit: Large, 55–more than 60mm. Conical-cylindrical, nose and base broad. Stem within or usually projecting slightly or distinctly from a deep, steep cavity. Eye basin variable, small or narrow and deep, slightly furrowed or crowned; calyx more or less open, sepals upright, reflexed at tips, often green. Skin primrose yellow or pale green; dry, rough; russet often scabrous in eye basin, spreading; lenticels large, russeted. Flush always, 30–65%, bright scarlet with crimson flecks. Flesh sweet without astringency; yellowish, vascular strands yellow; chewy.

Juice: SG 1054; acidity 0.20%; tannin 0.12%

Cider: No cider-maker's notes, but Le Bret is likely to make a soft, pleasant and light cider on its own.

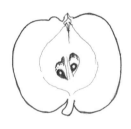

LISTENER

Very Early Sweet Cider or Dessert Apple

Listener trees may still be found north Devon and in the Tamar Valley where the variety probably originated. It is rather more use as an interesting dessert apple than for cider making. Trees are reputed to have some resistance to leaf scab. Flowers mid May

The fruits are lemon yellow, heavily ribbed barrel shape. Ready for picking August-September.

Fruit: Medium size, 45–60mm. Cylindrical with a broad flat nose and rounded base. Heavily ribbed from top to bottom, starting from the eye. Eye basin quite pinched and small. Eye tight closed with small green, rather upright sepals. Stem short [5–10mm] usually within or projecting slightly from a narrow, deep cavity. Skin smooth, pale greenish-yellow ripening to pale yellow, with a few light green dots. No flush. Flesh tender and juicy.

Juice: Very sweet but with a little acid in a good year.

Cider: It is early maturing and ready to make a little cider in time for Christmas but there are no Long Ashton notes.

LODERS

Mid Season Full Bittersweet Cider Apple

Preliminary names: Loders P [Puddletown] and M [Matravers]

Two similar trees were found during the DATA search for old Dorset cider apple trees, one by a gateway of a house called Matravers in Loders, near Bridport and another in a back garden in Puddletown near Dorchester. Our newly propagated trees from these sources were named Loders M and Loders P respectfully, but so far have proved to be the same variety [Distributed 2011]. Loders begins as a short nursery tree but grows to form a compact, regular and heavy cropping mature tree. Flowering mid season.

Its fruit are medium sized, conical, yellow-green, usually with an orange flush on the cheek and often with considerable russet. They are ready by mid October.

Fruit: Medium, 45–55mm. Flattened conical with a broad nose and base; often a little lop-sided and angular in section. Stem usually a stub within the narrow, deep, heavily russeted cavity. Eye basin small, shallow, fairly smooth. Eye usually open, sepals upright and long if not broken. Skin dry, with considerable russet spreading from the stem cavity across the cheeks as a network. Lenticels conspicuous as small brown dots. Colour yellow-green ripening to yellow, frequently up to half covered with a slightly speckled diffuse, bright cherry red or orange flush. Flesh mild bittersweet, chewy, greenish.

Juice: Astringent, rather thin, sweet.
SG 1060; acidity 0.20%; tannin 0.60%

Cider: Astringent, with a distinctive aroma, rather lactic and farmyardy but good.

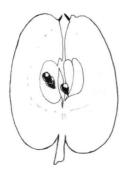

LONG TOM

Early Mid Season Mild Sharp Cider Apple

This variety seems to be a speciality peculiar to the North West corner of Somerset, Clevedon to Weston, Kingston Seymour and Congresbury area. It resembles an elongated version of the familiar Tom Putt and could well be a seedling from it, saved and cultivated for its curious distinctive shape. Long Tom is an early maturing dual purpose, mild sharp apple, ready by early October.

The unmistakable fruits are large, red striped and elliptical, with ten strongly marked ribs from top to bottom. The flesh is marbled with red throughout and the core is large and hollow so that the pips rattle when the fruits are ripe.

Fruit: Large, 55–60mm in diameter and up to 70mm tall. Elliptical, small nose, small rounded base; strongly 10 ribbed from eye to stem cavity. Stem projecting distinctly, rather fleshy, bulge at the tree end; cavity medium, rather narrow and deep. Eye basin slight, crowned, beaded and irregular similar to Tom Putt; calyx open, sepals short and closed. Skin pale yellow; rough and waxy; russet slight in each basin; lenticels small brown dots on lighter surround. Flush usually more or less complete; diffuse pink with bright red flecks, short stripes. Flesh mild sharp; juicy and melting, white, distinctly reddened under skin. Core open, large; seeds numerous, free rattling when ripe; tube a very deep cone extending to the core, pronounced stylar column.

Juice: Mild sharp.

Cider: No cider-maker's notes found. Long Tom would be a useful mild sharp for blending with juice from other fruit and on its own may even produce as good a result as Tom Putt.

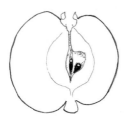

LORNA DOONE

Early Bittersharp Cider Apple

This variety was raised for the Lorna Doone cider company and many trees are still found in the orchard behind the old cider factory in Ford Street on the slopes of the Blackdown Hills near Wellington. Fruit was sent to Long Ashton in the 1930s from the factory by Mr E H Wells and it was given first prize in the 1935 cider competition as a good, medium sharp cider. The Report mentions the variety's reputation as a heavy cropper. It was considered especially interesting because of this and its high tannin content, but in spite of further successful cider trials, Lorna Doone does not seem to have been propagated much outside its native locality. Some trees exist in a trial orchard in Breinton, Hereford, and it is represented in the dessert apple section of the Brogdale Collection. If Lorna Doone still comes up to its prize-winning reputation, it would make a worthwhile addition to modern orchards, but it is a rather biennial and vigorously sprawling tree. Flowering mid season.

The fruits which are ready in mid October, are fairly large, flattened-conical with a stout stem in a deep cavity. The skin is pale yellowish, flushed red and similar to Somerset Redstreak.

Fruit: Medium to large, 55–more than 60mm. Flattened conical, broad base and nose; tending to ribbed. Stem short, stout, within a deep cavity. Eye basin medium, fairly smooth or slightly crowned with ribs sometimes extending down the sides. Eye open, sepals upright. Skin greasy. Russet dots and patches. Colour pale yellowish-green, usually more than half pale pink or light orange, lightly striped and flecked bright red from stem cavity becoming fainter towards the nose. Flesh mild bittersharp; sweet, chewy, yellowish.

Juice: SG 1060; acidity 0.43%; tannin 0.30%

Cider: Although prize-winning in 1935, Lorna Doone makes rather a strong flavoured cider with a harsh tannin character. It is best blended and should be a useful extender for low tannin mixtures.

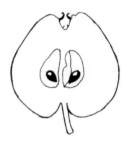

MAJOR

Early Bittersweet Cider Apple

Major most probably originated in mid Somerset, but it is also found in many traditional Devon cider orchards. It is an old variety which was included from time to time in pre1920 trial orchards. It became popular again in the late 1980s and 90s when it was often planted in bush orchards together with the other early varieties, Ashton Bitter, Ellis Bitter and White Jersey in order to extend the harvesting season forward to the end of September and very early October. As a standard Major forms a medium to large sized, round headed tree with spreading limbs. Bush trees are vigorous, even on the more dwarfing rootstocks, but have a good natural centre leader habit and spurs form quickly on the many spreading branches. Its excessive vigour is difficult to control on strong soils, but it makes and excellent manageable tree with an M9 interstock. Flowering time is late mid season. It is rather susceptible to canker, silverleaf and sometimes, scab.

The fruit is smallish, typical 'jersey' shaped, conical with a pointed nose, and covered in a light pinkish red striped flush. It begins to drop before the end of September but the apples do not keep well on the ground.

Fruit: Small to medium, rarely large, 45–60mm. Conical, base narrow, nose pointed; sometimes ribbed. Stem woody, level with the base or projecting distinctly, sometimes slightly from a small, sometimes slight cavity. Eye basin small, variable, usually shallow, puckered, irregular, usually ribbed, often slight corona present; calyx closed, sepals overlapping, often fairly long, reflexed at tips. Skin yellowish-green or pale yellow; smooth and slightly waxy; russet usually slight. Flush usually

35–65% or more, flecked and striped over diffuse, bright red; overall pinkish appearance. Flesh sweet, astringent with a pleasant fruity flavour; white, woolly, rather soft, juicy.

Juice: SG 1054; acidity 0.18%; tannin 0.41%

Cider: Major is a full bittersweet and makes a fruity cider of average quality. It is best blended with other varieties for a more balanced product.

MARLPITS LATE

Late Mid-Season Full Bittersweet Cider Apple

Preliminary name: MP1

This unknown variety was found principally West Dorset during the DATA Project search for lost Dorset cider apples. It was first seen in a garden in West Milton, near Bridport, one of three cider apple trees close to an old hedge. It forms very strong, upright, whippy tree, initially growing tall with few branches. Cropping soon becomes biennial. Our young trees in the nursery were very tall with few feathers [Distributed 2011]. Flowering mid season.

The fruits, ready late October, vary in size depending on the season. They are conical, yellowish-green usually with a pinkish/orange flush and often with some russet around the eye. Both the eye basin and the stem cavity are noticeably small and the stem short.

Fruit: Medium-large but variable, 45–>60mm. Flattened conical, sometimes tending to show a waist, with a broad flat nose and rounded base; roundly ribbed, often lopsided. Stem usually a stub within the very small cavity or projecting slightly. [3–6mm]. Eye basin usually small, shallow but occasionally deeper, often russeted. Eye closed. Skin dry, often rough with russet that spreads across the cheeks in a network. Lenticels sometimes conspicuous brown or red dots. Pale yellow or yellow-green, frequently with a trace of pinkish-red or orange flush. Flesh mild bittersweet, yellowish, chewy.

Juice: SG 0146; acidity 0.23%; tannin 0.40%. Hard tannin with a taste similar to Tremletts Bitter

Cider: Makes a very good single variety cider.

MARNHULL MILL

Early Full Sharp Cider Apple

Preliminary name: Marnhull 2A/B

This unknown variety recovered during the DATA Project search for lost Dorset cider apples was first found in the remnants of an orchard that once belonged to an old mill on the river Stour in Marnhull. The trees are quite small with compact rounded heads. They appear to be performing healthily still, if a little scabby, in spite of their neglect in an overgrown site. Our nursery trees were short and compact but had a good number of useful feathers [Distributed 2011]. The leaves are very large with a long pointed tip and smooth, rounded crenulations on the margins. Hopefully Marnhull Mill will perform well on a good site and appropriate rootstock.

The primrose yellow apples we collected in early October varied in size but many were quite large, slightly waisted conical with a broad, flat nose.

Fruit: Medium-large, 50–60mm. Conical, slightly waisted with a broad, flat nose and rounded base; rather ribbed in section. Stem projecting slightly [5–10mm] from quite a narrow, heavily russeted cavity. Eye basin quite broad but shallow and slightly crowned. Eye open, sepals free and reflexed. Skin dry. Scab susceptible. Yellow green ripening to primrose yellow, frequently with a trace of pinkish-orange flush. Flesh sharp, melting, yellowish.

Juice: Our poor sample was rather flavourless and grassy.
SG 1056; acidity 1.51%; tannin 0.29%

Cider: Probably best blended with a less sharp variety.

MEADOW COTTAGE

Early Bittersweet Cider Apple

Preliminary name: Mill Lane 1

An unknown variety recovered during the DATA Project search for lost Dorset cider apples, first found in a small field [opposite Meadow Cottage], close to the old mill on the river Stour in Marnhull. The tree was quite large and relatively healthy with a full crop of fruit. Our nursery trees [Distributed 2011] were nice looking, tall and vigorous with many good feathers and dards. The leaves are very large and round with small crenulations on the margins. This early maturing variety should have a promising future.

Meadow Cottage apples will start dropping early in October. They are small, conical and green with a spotty red flush on some.

Fruit: Small-medium, 40–45mm. Conical with a small nose and small rounded base; rounded in section. Stem virtually absent or just a stub in a small cavity. Eye basin absent or just a slight indentation, occasionally just showing beading or slightly puckered. Eye open, sepals short or broken. Skin waxy. Occasionally some russet on the stem or eye basins. Lenticels occasionally show as small red or brown dots. Pale green ripening to yellow green, frequently less than a third covered with a slight, bright red speckling of dots. Flesh bittersweet, chewy, pale yellowish.

Juice: Sweet, astringent, full and floral.
SG 1075; acidity 0.23%; tannin 0.39%

Cider: Should make a useful bittersweet contribution to a mix.

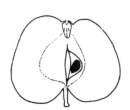

MÉDAILLE D'OR

Late Full Bittersweet Cider Apple

Synonym: Spreading Médaille d'Or

This French variety, brought here by the Woolhope Naturalists Club in 1884, is noticeable for its very high and harsh tannin content. It was widely planted around the 1920s in Herefordshire and later in the 1952 series of Long Ashton trial orchards. It is a parent of the new apple, Late Gold which has inherited its tannin character in a reasonably grower friendly tree. Médaille d'Or trees are small with a dense round head but are very susceptible to breakage and thus, a short life expectancy. Although its vintage qualities are good, it is not an easy orchard tree, but rather one for the connoisseur. Yields can be high but often only every other year. Flowering very late May.

The fruits are small, round golden and russeted and are held in clusters. Ready by the end of November.

Fruit: Small, 40–45mm. Conical-cylindrical: tending to ribbed. Stem variable, thin and woody, usually projecting from a large deep cavity. Eye basin large, deep, smooth. Eye slightly open, sepals often green. Skin smooth, dry, usually yellow or greenish-yellow. Considerable russet network. Usually resistant to scab. Sometimes with a slight diffuse pink-orange or orange-yellow flush. Flesh sweet, heavy astringency; white, soft, dry..

Juice: SG 1059; acidity 0.27%; tannin 0.64%

Cider: Full astringent bittersweet. Often alcoholic and fruity. Good quality.

MICHELIN

Mid Season Bittersweet Cider Apple

This is a French variety introduced into Hereford by a Monsieur Legrand for the Woolhope Society in 1884. It was named after a Monsieur Michelin who did much to promote the study of cider fruits. Michelin was extensively planted in Hereford from the 1920s, and it is currently the most widely planted variety in all the cider growing areas. Although its juice qualities are only modest, it is one of the most reliably annual cropping varieties along with Dabinett and this is the main reason for its popularity. However, its rather stiff, fastigiate habit allows its fruit to be shaken off prematurely towards the end of the season, frequently before it is properly free of starch and unsuitable for cider making. Further planting is presently being discouraged by major cider companies for this reason. Mature standard trees are medium sized with stiff, upright limbs. As a bush tree, it tends to want to be multi-leadered, and needs considerable thought and training in its formative years to produce a good centre-leader shape. Spurring is quick and good, and cropping starts early. Flowering time is 2nd week of May. Unfortunately, it is very prone to canker, especially on some sites and young trees can be almost destroyed by the disease.

Plain green Michelin apples are never very large, rather elongated conical with a small nose, a rounded base and distinctly ribbed. They are properly mature by mid October.

Fruit: Medium often small, 40–50mm. Conical, cylindrical, sometimes pointed; distinctly ribbed. Stem thick, woody, often fleshy, sometimes off-set, usually projecting considerably, sometimes level with base; stem cavity well defined. Eye basin shallow or slight, puckered, often beaded; calyx closed, sepals often green. Skin greenish-yellow to yellow; smooth, slightly waxy; sometimes russet spreads from stem cavity to cheek; lenticels often conspicuous; scab susceptible. Sometimes flushed, usually slight pinky-orange diffuse. Flesh sweet with some astringency; white, woolly.

Juice: SG 1050; acidity 0.25%; tannin 0.23%

Cider: Medium bittersweet with soft tannin.

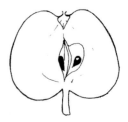

MORGAN SWEET
Early Sweet Cider Apple

Well known to many living in North Somerset, its natural home, Morgan sweet is cherished and extolled from happy childhood memories. It was once widely planted all over Somerset and to a lesser extent in Devon and Gloucestershire, originally intended as a 'pot' fruit or cooker, much of it going to South Wales distributed by Morgan of Cardiff. But once it lost that fresh fruit market, Morgan Sweet had to go for cider making only, then often fetching a lower price than other genuine cider fruits. The fruit matures very early and its juice ferments very rapidly. For some farms and cider-makers Morgan Sweet is popular for making an early cider, ready for Christmas, well before the main cider finishes maturing properly. Morgan Sweet flowers early to mid season but it is no use as a pollinator. It makes very strong growth, forming a big spreading tree with large, scab susceptible leaves. It has been widely used as a stem builder for standard trees but its strong framework growth often takes over in the head of a weaker variety.

The large, pale yellow fruits are easy to distinguish from similar but bittersweet Bulmers Norman by their pure sweet taste. They ripen very early in September, often dropping and rotting on the ground and going to waste.

Fruit: Medium to very large, 50–more than 60mm. Conical, base flattened, nose pointed; usually ribbed; king fruits elongated. Stem thin, woody; usually projecting slightly from a medium, shallow cavity; king fruit stems thick, fleshy and short. Eye basin medium, shallow, sometimes large and deep, ribbed or puckered; calyx usually closed, sepals touching, free, often green at the base. Skin greenish-yellow; smooth, dry, sometimes slightly waxy; scab susceptible; russet usually confined to stem cavity; lenticels often conspicuous, concentrated around the eye. Flush absent, occasionally very slight red flecks spreading from the eye. Flesh sweet with no astringency; white, rather soft and juicy.

Juice: SG 1049; acidity 0.22%; tannin 0.13%; nitrogen 18mg/100mg [average 5–10mg/100mg]

Cider: Morgan Sweet is a pure sweet. Because of its high nitrogen content the juice will ferment very rapidly. With care it can produce a good quality cider with a strong, persistently fruity flavour but lacking in body.

NÉHOU

Early Maturing Full Bittersweet Cider Apple

This variety was introduced into this country from France in the 1920s by H P Bulmers, useful for its early maturity. It was at one time well known and widely distributed but fell out of favour because its large, soft, early fruits bruise easily and rot quickly when they fall. It was often planted in Herefordshire and to a lesser extent in some of the older Taunton Cider orchards in the 1970s. It matures rather too early for commercial cider production and many trees have now been replaced by more reliable and slightly later maturing varieties. It makes a small to medium sized tree with a rounded head that is dense, twiggy and scab susceptible. It flowers early mid season.

The distinctive conical, greasy butter-yellow apples are easily identified by their juiciness and fruity tannin. Ready late September-early October.

Fruit: Small-medium, 40–50mm. Conical with a flat base; tendency to ribbing. Stem medium, 10–12mm, woody, sometimes off-set, projecting slightly from deep, narrow, often slightly russeted cavity. Eye basin rather small, shallow rather irregular, corona of beads usually present. Eye closed, sepals long. Skin smooth, dry, sometimes slightly waxy or greasy. Lenticels variable, concentrated around the eye, sometime conspicuous, sometimes large and irregular, sometimes surrounded with a pink area. Scab susceptible. Colour yellow, rarely with a little pinkish-orange flush spreading from the eye. Flesh sweet and astringent; white, soft, juicy.

Juice: SG 1057; malic 0.17%; tannin 0.60%

Cider: Full bittersweet, astringent, fruity, full bodied and of good to excellent quality.

NETHERTON LATE BLOWER

Late Sweet Cider Apple

Synonym: Town Farm 59

This old Devon variety is found as older trees in the Exeter area and more widespread as young trees. Netherton Late Blower was discovered in 1995 as Town Farm 59 by Kevin Croucher of Thornhayes Nursery who now propagates and distributes it by its true name. It came from an old trial orchard at East Worlington Nr Crediton. Netherton Late Blower is listed in the RHS Exhibition of 1934 as a sweet kitchen apple, but earlier in 1884, Hogg described it as *'A Devon cider apple in much favour. The tree bears freely and the fruit keeps well. Its skin is so thick that birds will not injure the fruit.'* Its juice is low in both acid and tannin, confirming its place as a Devon pure sweet cider apple. Trees are moderately vigorous and spreading with age. Once scab free it is now scab susceptible.

The apples are rather flattened or oblate, covered in a mauveish-pink flush a few short red streaks. Ready late and will keep till December.

Fruit: Medium to large, 55–60mm. Flattened conical to oblate, sometimes very lopsided. Stem very short, thick and fleshy in a small, golden russeted cavity. Eye small and half closed, in a narrow puckered basin. Skin greenish-yellow. Rather scabby. About half covered with a pale red flecked mauveish-pink flush and distinct crimson stripes on the base. Flesh sweet with little acidity; firm and juicy with a woolly texture,.

Juice: Sweet SG 1058; acidity 0.20%; tannin 0.12%

Cider: No Long Ashton notes.

NINE SQUARE

Dual Purpose Sharp Cider Apple

Synonyms: Devonshire Nine Square, Nine Square Pippin or sometimes even Four Square

This is a very old apple, probably originally from the Tamar Valley. It was recorded as a cider apple in 1824 but it is probably much older. It is now propagated by several nurseries and has been widely adopted in the western counties. It can be found especially in Devon, in Cornwall, Somerset and even near Bridport in Dorset where it was growing in company with Colloggett Pippin. Nine Square trees are very vigorous, spreading like a Bramley. It is fairly scab resistant. It crops well but can be rather biennial. Flowers early May.

Nine Square apples are easy to recognise, tall and boxy with a knobbly nose. Ready early October and stores until December.

Fruit: Large-very large, 55–>60mm. Tall cylindrical, boxy, with a knobbly, flat nose and small flat base. Rather lopsided, distinctly angular and ribbed. Stem variable, sometimes a stub, sometimes just projecting from the deep, narrow cavity, sometimes quite long [15mm]. Eye basin small, usually shallow and narrow, often beaded and irregular with five crowns. Eye closed, sepals long. Skin pale green ripening to yellow-green, frequently with a pinky-red blush, brighter red on the broad side. Core large and open. Flesh sharp; greenish, juicy and chewy. Juice usually with a good sugar content. But no records of its use for cider.

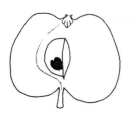

NORTHWOOD

Late Sweet Cider Apple

Synonym: Sweet Woodbine in Devon

This is a typical sweet Devon cider apple probably originated somewhere in the Crediton area where it is still often found today . It sometimes occurs in West Dorset and south west Somerset. It was originally called Woodbine because it develops an aroma similar to honeysuckle when it is stored. Northwood was included in the earliest Long Ashton trial orchards planted before 1920 and also in the 1957 series. Although it is slow to get going and need a little longer in training, it is a good quality late harvesting variety that deserves to be planted more. Fortunately it is now becoming more popular and is propagated by several nurseries. Northwood trees are medium to large, with a neat round head, but cropping can be biennial. It may still be scab resistant. Flowers mid May with attractive cream coloured blossoms.

The fruits which are smooth skinned, rather cylindrical and usually half covered in a light red flecked flush, are ready in October but will keep for more than 3 weeks.

Fruit: Medium 45–55mm. Flattened conical or cylindrical, slight ribbing. Stem variable, usually projecting clearly from a shallow cavity. Eye basin varies, medium to large and slightly irregular. Eye open, sepals free, long and reflexed at the tip if not broken. Skin smooth, yellowish-green. Usually about half covered with diffuse, flecked flush, striped with darker red. Flesh sweet lacking astringency; slightly crisp, white or greenish-white, quite juicy.

Juice: SG 1049; acidity 0.27%; tannin 0.17%

Cider: Sweet, soft, fruity and good quality, often with an interesting woody aroma.

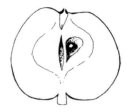

NORTON BITTERS

Late Full Bittersweet Cider Apple

Synonym: Nerton Bitter

Norton Bitters was recorded for the Bath and West in 1895 as growing in Mr F J Hayes' Orchard in West Pennard, and a contemporary watercolour of it together with three other old Somerset cider apples, still hangs on the wall of the Secretary's Office at the Showground at Shepton Mallet. Trees still exist in this area and it was also planted in one or two places in Hereford by H P Bulmer after fruit was brought to Long Ashton in 1964. It was never propagated extensively in either county although it probably deserves to be more widely planted.

Norton Bitters apples are dark red-maroon, rather cylindrical in shape, with very small eye and stem basins. They are often covered with patches of russet. The taste is a good, often full bittersweet, but maturing in November makes the variety rather too late for general orchard use.

Fruit: Medium; usually 45–55mm. Flattened conical or cylindrical; rounded or slightly angular, sometimes slightly lopsided. Stem usually a stub within the cavity, sometimes projecting slightly from a small, narrow cavity; stem cavity non-existent or very slight in king fruit. Eye basin small or slight, narrow and shallow, smooth or irregularly beaded; sepals short, green. Skin yellow; smooth or rough, dry or slightly waxy; russet often spreading from eye, patches or network over cheek. Always more than two thirds, often more or less completely flushed diffuse dark red, striped bright red. Some fruits only lightly striped with no diffuse flush. Flesh mild or full bittersweet with good flavour; melting when ripe, white or greenish, sometimes reddened near nose.

Juice: SG 1068; acidity 0.26%; tannin 0.23%

Cider: No comments are recorded at Long Ashton, but Norton Bitter is a medium to full bittersweet with good flavour and aroma, so should make a pleasant single variety cider or blend usefully with other varieties.

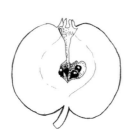

PAIGNTON MARIGOLD

Sub-Acid Dual Purpose Cider/Dessert Apple

Synonym: Nelson

Found plentifully in the Paignton area of South Devon, Paignton Marigold is now propagated by several nurseries. This is really an eating apple that came from the same stable as the sharp cider Browns Apple, R J Hill's Nursery, Barkington Manor, Staverton, Totnes in the mid 1960s. Like Browns Apple, it was totally scab free at that time but now seems to have lost its resistance. It has a good compact tree habit and moderate vigour but is rather susceptible to blossom wilt. Flowers early May.

The handsome fruits are large, cylindrical, pinkish, striped bright red and yellow. Ready October.

Fruit: Medium to large 45–60mm. Conical tending to cylindrical, broad base and flat nose; tending to lopsided. Stem projecting slightly or distinctly from a deep narrow russeted cavity, sometimes off-set with a bulge on the base of the fruit. Eye basin medium size, smooth or slightly puckered. Eye open, sepals long, upright. Skin smooth, becoming shiny and waxy. Prominent, often green lenticels. Yellow-green with some streaks of russet, always more than half covered with an attractive bright red diffuse and darker flecked flush. Flesh sub-acid sharp; white, juicy, and crisp.

Juice: SG 1054; acidity 1.00%; tannin 0.12%

Cider: No Long Ashton notes. Cider is likely to be thin and lacking in character.

PAYHEMBURY

Mid-season Dual Purpose Apple

Said to be a local apple, probably from Payhembury village relatively recently, it is now propagated by several nurseries and popularly grown in orchards around the area just north of Exeter as a juice apple. Some good specimens are growing in the new orchard behind the Ranger's Yard at NT Killerton House. These trees are strong growing. It is a variety that is reputed to be scab free and well suited to growing in wetter areas.

Payhembury is a large green 'cooking apple'. It should be ready early to mid October and said to keep well, holding its flavour.

Fruit: Exceptionally large, 80–90mm. Flattened conical or oblate, narrow nose and very flat base. Very angular and distinctly ribbed. Stem a fleshy stub within a broad but shallow cavity lined with scarf skin. Eye basin slight, narrow and shallow, crowned, irregular, bumpy, even furrowed. Eye open, sepals long, free, green and reflexed. Skin overall pale green. Flesh greenish, browning rapidly, chewy and with a sharp culinary taste.

Juice: Sharp. Excellent for juicing.

Cider: No Long Ashton notes.

PENNARD BITTER

Early Bittersweet Cider Apple

Synonyms: Possibly Meare Bitter but this may be a similar, closely related variety

Named after the village of West Pennard near Shepton Mallet in Somerset, Pennard Bitter is said to have been propagated by Harold Heal of Windmill Hill, Glastonbury, probably towards the end of the 19th Century. It makes a vigorous, spreading bush tree and seems to crops well and regularly but is hardly ever grown on a dwarfing stock. It could be useful in bush orchards and probably deserves to be grown more widely as an early harvesting variety.

Pennard Bitter apples are typically large, green, flattened and angular with brownish red russeted flush and a very short stalk. It ripens early in October.

Fruit: Large to very large, 55mm to more than 60mm. Oblate conical, nose rounded, base broad; rather angular, distinctly ribbed. Stem thick, green and fleshy stub within the cavity; cavity small, tight. Eye basin medium, narrow, deep, furrowed; calyx closed, sepals long. Skin yellowish-green; usually smooth and dry, sometimes rough with russet; russet slight, sometimes considerable, spreading from both cavities as a light network over the flush. Flush always 30–65%, diffuse dark orange red or brown, resembling Cox. Flesh medium bittersweet; juicy, chewy, greenish, browning rapidly when cut.

Juice: SG 1060; acidity 0.18%; tannin 0.32%

Cider: No cider-maker's notes have been found but Pennard Bitter looks like a useful bittersweet with plenty of tannin, suitable for blending with other varieties.

PIG'S NOSE

Early Sub-acid Dual Purpose Apple

Synonym: Pig's Snout

There are probably many variants of Pig's Nose to be found in Cornwall, Devon, south Somerset and Dorset. Many have been rediscovered in the area around the Tamar valley, numbered and catalogued by fruit enthusiasts James Evans and Mary Martin and these are considered to be the true variety. All Pig's Noses have the same basic shape and character; conical, waisted with a distinct nose, and often brightly striped red and yellow but may vary in size. Probably many trees are retained out of curiosity and tradition rather than for the cidermaking qualities of the apples. The full description below is of a 'true' Pig's Nose from and old orchard in Milton Abbot on the Cornwall/Devon border.

Pig's Noses are characteristically snouted, orangey-red and yellow striped apples of varying sizes. Ready early-mid October depending on the selection.

Fruit: Can be small but often quite large, 45–>60mm. Conical, waisted with a tall flat nose and a broad, flat base; ribbed from the nose down and rather angular. Eye basin small, narrow but often quite deep, puckered with shallow furrows. Eye open or pinched closed. Stem often absent or a stub within the large, broad, deep cavity, often lined with heavy rough russet. Skin smooth, slightly waxy and yellow-green to golden, usually half covered in bright red broad, short stripes. It appears rather orangey-red overall. Flesh yellowish, often reddened under the skin on the flushed side, juicy, crisp.

Juice: Has a surprisingly good cider flavour.

Cider: The well flavoured, mild sharp juice with a good sugar content should make a reasonable contribution to early cider. But note that not all the variant Noses may be as useful.

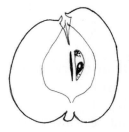

PLUM APPLE

Sub-Acid Apple

Occasionally trees bearing fruit resembling plums in shape and colour occur in North West Devon. They fit the description of Plum Apple in Hogg's Manual of 1884, *'A remarkable apple for its shape and colour'*. But he does not mention the variety in his *Apples and Pears as Vintage Fruit.* This description comes from apples collected from an orchard in Milton Abbot, planted in 1938–43, and the illustration, from a tree near Eggesford in central Devon.

Purple plum look-alikes. Ready late and keep till Christmas.

Fruit: Small-medium size 40–50mm. Elliptical with hardly any base and a small flattened nose; roundly ribbed. Stem short, projecting slightly from a very small cavity. Eye more or less open, basin smooth, irregularly beaded. Sepals green, pinched together. Always completely covered with a strong dark maroon diffuse flush, with brownish patches on the shady side. Flesh dry, rather chewy, greenish, tasting sub-acid.

Juice: According to Hogg '. . . *sweet and agreeably though not richly flavoured.'*

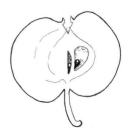

PLYMPTON PIPPIN

Sub-Acid Dual Purpose Apple

This is a relatively new discovery re-introduced into the far West. Although not a true cider apple, it does have a chewy, cider texture. It is now readily available and gaining popularity.

The apples are very large, bright green with a distinctively folded, crowned and pleated eye. Ready late October,

Fruit: Large-very large, 55–>60mm. Oblate; angular and strongly ribbed, sometimes lopsided. Stem variable, sometimes a stub, can project considerably [stub, 7–28mm] from a fairly shallow, gold russeted cavity. Eye basin small and narrow, folded and gathered, surrounded by shallow crowns. Sepals broad, green and eye open. Skin smooth, dry, dark green ripening to bright green. Lenticels sometimes brown dots on flush. Russet patchy and spreading from stem. Flush usually up to a third light pink to brownish-red, short stripes. Flesh sub-acid, hard, chewy, greenish.

POLLY WHITEHAIR
Early Sub-acid Apple

It is thought to have originated from the Truro district where is called Pigs Nose [not to be confused with Pig's Snout]. There is a similar variety called Polly but the 'true' Polly Whitehair is unlikely to be found outside Cornwall. The apples are small and neatly shaped and were once used for pickling although the Cornish tradition of pickling apples whole, is now almost lost. They do taste rather insipid and probably traditionally went mostly for cider rather than cooking. Polly's biggest claim to fame is its mass of white blossom in spring. Trees produce laterals freely and crop at an early age. Flowering mid May.

The apples are small, green cylinders, ready early September but they store well late into the season.

Fruit: Medium-large [50–60mm], conical or cylindrical with a broad flat nose and a rounded base. Slightly ribbed on the body, ending in irregular crowns above the eye. Eye basin broad and shallow. Stem short but just showing from a narrow, deep cavity, often offset with a bulge at the base. Skin pale green ripening to yellowish-green, shiny and quite waxy. Sometimes with a fine netted russet and russet dots. Scab susceptible. Flesh greenish-white, soft, sweet to sub-acid, often rather non-descript taste.

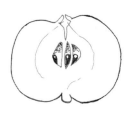

PONSFORD
Late Dual Purpose Sharp Apple

Widely propagated and well-known in old orchards especially in East-Mid Devon, Ponsford is probably a very old 19th century variety from the Crediton area. It is a useful and popular farm apple for cider and for the kitchen. It cooks well and keeps its shape. It is probably a triploid so growth strong, ultimately forming a large tree with erect habit. Crops maybe slow to come but are very good once the tree is established. Flowers 2–3rd week May.

The apples are often very large, rather flattened conical, green, often red striped Ready late October-November and will keep through the winter till April.

Fruit: Very large, 55–70mm but can be up to 90mm. Flattened conical or oblate with a broad flat nose and base. Often lopsided and tending to angular in section. Stem variable, usually a stub or sometimes projecting slightly from a narrow deep cavity. Eye basin broad, shallow, crowned and irregular. Eye open. Skin grass green to dull dark green. Frequently up to half covered with dark red or orange diffuse flush, flecked or striped red. Sometimes just green with only a trace of pinkish-orange flush. Flesh mildly sharp; greenish, juicy.

Juice: SG 1045; acidity 0.66%; tannin 0.10%
Sugar content often low but juice yield good.

Cider: Body light. Fermentation inclined to be rapid.

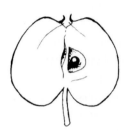

PORTERS PERFECTION

Late Medium Bittersharp Cider Apple

Synonym: Clusters

This variety originated in nurseryman Mr Charles Porter's nursery at East Lambrook during the 19th century. Some fruit from the original tree was sent to Long Ashton in 1907 where it was judged remarkable for the quality of its juice. From this start it was quickly propagated and distributed around some of the early trial orchards and again in the 1957 series of trials. The variety is fairly common in the Martock area of Somerset and appears less regularly in other parts of the county. Porter's Perfection is closely related to Lambrook Pippin and their fruits are very similar, but it is remarkable for regularly producing fused fruits, usually two together, sometimes three to five in one. This curious phenomena that also occurs more rarely in the varieties Lambrook Pippin, Dabinett and Somerset Redstreak. Porter's Perfection is a reputedly scab resistant and vigorous grower with a spreading habit and drooping branches. Mature trees are large to medium sized and produce heavy crops of small fruit. Flowering time is early May.

Porter's Perfection is late and not ready for harvest until the third week of November. Its fruits are small and dark red with conspicuously light spots round the lenticels. Look out for fused fruits. (See top of page 33).

Fruit: Small, sometimes medium; 40–50mm. Flattened conical or conical; some fused fruits consisting of 2–5 apples usually present. Stem thick, slightly fleshy, often green, projecting considerably, sometimes slightly from a small, shallow, often irregular cavity. Eye basin shallow; calyx open, sepals fairly long, upright and reflexed at tips. Skin greenish-yellow; smooth, slightly waxy; russet slight in the stem cavity; lenticels conspicuous, small, surrounded by lighter patch on flush, or green patch where flush is absent. More than two thirds flushed, flecked and striped dark red. Flush usually absent from the shaded portions of the fruit. Flesh mild sharp with some astringency; white or greenish-white, sometimes reddened below skin, crisp and juicy.

Juice: SG 1054; acidity 0.82%; tannin 0.25%

Cider: Porter's Perfection can produce an excellent cider. Its juice is rather acidic bittersharp and is better blended for a more balanced product.

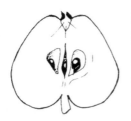

RED JERSEY

Late Mid Season Bittersweet Cider Apple

Synonyms: Laurel Grains, Laurel Grange, also Loral or Loyal Drain or Drang!

A typical small Somerset 'jersey' apple. Trees are still found commonly around the Shepton Mallet to Glastonbury area. It was recorded at the Bath and West Show in 1895 from West Pennard. The curious synonyms by which Red Jersey has been known have arisen through miss-spellings or perhaps miss-hearings of the local Somerset way of speaking. It was originally called Laurel Grains, referring to the small size of the fruit. Trees also still occur in some of the old Long Ashton trial orchards and in farm orchards, mostly in Somerset and adjacent parts of Devon. Red Jersey trees are quite distinctive, medium to large size with a spreading habit and a heavy, complex system of twigs and spurs forming a dense crown. Its leaves are also distinctive, very numerous, narrow and rather greyish in appearance. It is a very late flowering variety and cropping is heavy but biennial. It is susceptible to scab.

The fruits are small, conical and flushed bright red. They have a tendency to drop prematurely in an on year, before the apples are properly mature, which should not be before mid October .

Fruit: Small, 40–55mm. Conical, narrow with a rather pointed nose; rounded. Stem small, woody, projecting slightly from a small, narrow cavity. Eye basin small to medium, puckered, sometimes ribbed, sometimes the ribs extend a short distance over cheek. Skin greenish-yellow; smooth, dry; russet confined to stem cavity, sometimes scaly; lenticels conspicuous; variable in size, small pale area surrounding; scab susceptible. Always more than 75% flushed and flecked, slightly diffuse red, sometimes dull, brownish red. Flesh sweet and astringent; white, slightly crisp, juicy.

Juice: SG 1052; acidity 0.20%; tannin 0.48%

Cider: Red Jersey makes a good quality, full bodied bittersweet cider. Its strong astringent tannin is too pronounced to use alone. Sugar content is average and fermentation slow.

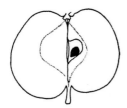

REINETTE OBRY

Late Medium Sharp Cider Apple

Synonym: Cadbury. Not to be confused with the Royal Wildling Cadbury of Hereford

Recent research suggests that Reinette Obry may well be one and the same as the old West Country variety, Cadbury. Reinette Obry was reputedly introduced from France by Robert Neville-Grenville of Butleigh Court, Somerset at the turn of the last century but no record of its origins have ever been found. The variety Cadbury was recorded by the Bath and West Society in 1898 and fruit from it was often sent to Long Ashton in the early years of the last century, mainly from mid and south Somerset. It seems likely that Neville-Grenville may have given this Cadbury the new name Reinette Cadbury, to distinguish it from the smooth skinned Hereford bittersweet Royal Wildling Cadbury, one that still exists only as a few old trees in trial orchards. Since it was also originally listed as Reinette Dobry or d'Obry, is reasonable to assume that there could have been a distortion of the word Cadbury on a poorly written record. The 'true' Cadbury is still occasionally found in the remnants of old orchards in south Somerset, some from the village of Cadbury itself, some over the border in north Dorset, even as far east as Shaftsbury. A number of old trees line a field near Maiden Newton.

Reinette Obry is a shy bearer, very slow to come into cropping but it can be very long lived. It performs well as a bush tree once it gets going. Young trees have stout upright shoots with very short internodes. Growth is good and mature trees are a good size if rather erect and heavily spurred. Flowering mid May.

The apples, ready in mid October-early November October, are greenish-yellow, paling as they ripen, with a very little flush, distinct lenticels and often considerable russeting.

Fruit: Medium to large, 55–more than 60mm. Oblate or flattened conical, with broad, rounded nose and base; rounded in section, sometimes rather ribbed. Stem short [5–10mm], usually within a small, deep, golden russeted cavity. Eye basin medium, narrow, deep, sometimes faintly crowned; eye usually open, sepals upright, green. Skin pale greenish-yellow ripening to pale butter yellow;

dry; covered with a distinctive network of russet, but sometimes without russet; lenticels corky, occasionally reddened. Occasionally a trace of pinkish-orange flush on some fruit. Flesh mildly acidic with a pleasant flavour; white, slightly crisp, juicy.

Juice: SG 1058; acidity 0.60%; tannin 0.15%

Cider: Useful all-round, fair body. Reinette Obry makes an excellent juice.

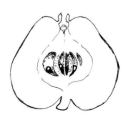

SERCOMBES NATURAL

Early Bittersweet Cider Apple

This variety is found in East Devon, especially in the Exe valley, possibly originating from Dunsford. A sample came to Long Ashton from Gray's Cider, Tedburn St Mary in 1955 as a local variety that showed some promise for early cidermaking. It also grows in some of Whiteways old orchards in Whimple where it was chosen for its heavy bittersweet juice. The trees have an upright habit, are heavy croppers but very prone to scab. Flowers mid-season.

Sercombes Natural apples are rounded, butter yellow usually with a few short, bright red stripes. Ready for harvest early in September

Fruit: Medium, 45–60mm. Usually tall conical, can be rather waisted with a distinct broad flat 'nose', often ribbed. Stem usually short [<5mm] and within a large, deep russeted cavity. Eye basin medium, fairly smooth or gathered, sometimes beaded. Eye tight closed or slightly open, sepals upright, green at base. Skin pale greenish-yellow ripening to butter yellow. Often very scabby. Lenticels widely spaced small brown dots, sometimes spreading into a fine russet network. Rarely a slight pink-orange flush or short red stripes. Flesh bittersweet; white.

Juice: Heavily bittersweet.

Cider: Although there are no cider makers records, it is said to be vintage quality.

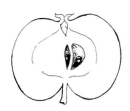

SEVERN BANK

Sub-acid Dual Purpose Apple

Described in the National Apple register as a mid season sharp, this variety was first recorded in 1884. It was grown in the 19th century in the Severn valley as an eating apple for the markets in Gloucester and the Midlands and still occurs infrequently as a cider apple in the South West.

The apples are large, heavy and green with a dark red flush. Ready late October.

Fruit: Large-very large, 55–>60mm. Flattened conical, often more oblate; often lopsided with a tendency to ribs on the top half. Stem projecting slightly or distinctly [5–15mm] from a deep, narrow cavity filled with green-gold russet. Eye basin broad and shallow, rather irregular or bumpy surround. Skin smooth, slightly waxy. Occasional patches of russet especially on flush. Lenticels as green or brown dots on the flush only. Coloured pale bright green, usually more than half covered with a diffuse, slightly flecked and striped dark red maroon flush. Flesh mild sharp, greenish, crisp and melting, juicy.

Juice: Mild sharp.

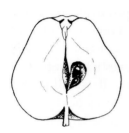

SHEEP'S NOSE

Mid Season Mild Sharp Cider Apple

Synonym: Also called Bell. Not to be confused with Pig's Nose

This is one of many aptly named cider apples known as Sheep's Nose, a generic name, but the one described here is distinctive and common enough to be considered a variety. It looks very much like a pale Bell Apple, which is also known as Sweet Sheep's Nose, but in this case its juice and flesh taste mildly sharp with no astringency. This one is most like the Sheep's Nose in the Brogdale collection, which is Sheep's Nose No.3 of the National Apple Register. Our Sheep's Nose lacks the attractive strong, pinkish scarlet stripes of the Sheep's Nose, described by Hogg, which is most likely the one described above as Pig's Nose. Our version matures quite late in October or November. The trees are small and whippy, with a weeping habit bearing some bare wood.

The large, heavy fruits are conical with a distinct nose, lightly flushed on the cheek, not unlike a large and aromatic Yarlington Mill.

Fruit: Large; 55–more than 60mm. Variable, basically conical, nose small, base flat, usually convex or distinctly waisted; rather angular. Stem woody, level with the base or projecting slightly, sometimes reddened; cavity deep, narrow. Eye basin small, narrow, often deep, some fruits with a curious raised line surrounding nose, crowned, somewhat irregular; sepals fairly long, green, more or less upright. Skin pale yellow-green; rough and dry; russet sometimes spreading in patches or streaks; lenticels small brown dots or large russeted; scab susceptible. Frequently 10–25% flushed, speckled and occasionally slightly striped pinkish-crimson or brownish-orange. Flesh sub-acid or mild sharp; juicy and melting.

Juice: SG 1045; acidity 0.25%; tannin 0.17%

Cider: No cidermaker's notes found, but Sheep's Nose is unlikely to contribute more than an average dual purpose apple to a cider.

SILVER CUP

Late Mid Season Medium Bittersweet Cider Apple

This variety was recorded at the Bath and West Show in 1899 and rated in the early part of the century as a useful bittersweet for blending. It was planted in many orchards in Devon and Somerset where it is still found as old trees, and was included in several trial orchards. It probably originated in south east Somerset, around Wincanton. Early records at Long Ashton were from fruit sent from this region between 1904–11, when it was obviously prized for the strength of its tannin. It is only grown as standard trees which are very upright and twiggy with many thin shoots and characteristically small leaves. Rather slow to form a tree, Silver Cup is shy at first but produces heavy crops every other year later. The size of the apples can vary. They can be large in light years or very small with heavy crops. Flowering time is early to mid May.

The apples are pale yellow conical with a noticeably deep-set eye, and ready for harvest from mid to late October but rot quickly on the ground.

Fruit: Variable, usually small, 40mm. to very large, more than 60mm. Conico-cylindrical, base broad; lopsided, angular with distinct ribs. Stem thick and woody, variable, within the cavity or sometimes projecting distinctly; cavity large and deep, or medium and shallow. Eye basin small, narrow, deep, irregular, furrowed or slightly beaded; calyx closed, sepals long, reflexed, green at the base. Skin pale yellow; smooth, slightly waxy or dry; no longer scab resistant; sometimes light russet, slight in stem cavity; lenticels conspicuous with pale surround or mauveish spots on flush. Usually less than 30% flushed diffuse brown to orange yellow. Flesh bittersweet; chewy, greenish, browning rapidly when cut.

Juice: SG 1075; acidity 0.15%; tannin 0.34%

Cider: Silver Cup makes a medium dry cider, rich and full bodied with a marked bitterness. It has a pleasant aroma and good flavour but a hard tannin aftertaste. The juice sugar content is often high but fermentation slow. This variety is very useful for blending.

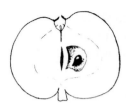

SLACK-MA-GIRDLE

Late Sweet Cider Apple Cider Apple

Synonyms: Slack-my-Girl, Woodbine

This variety must have earned some reputation for relaxing the inhibitions of young ladies on dates. It is also reputed to be good for jam making! As a cider apple, it resembles Woodbine both in looks and in the final product, and is sometimes incorrectly called by that name. Slack-ma-Girdle is more frequently seen in Devon orchards than Woodbine which is more common in Somerset. The differing tree habits are the best feature to distinguish between the two varieties. Trees of Slack-ma-Girdle are strong, a good size, upright at first then forming a compact head with numerous limbs. Woodbine trees are generously open with a few long spreading limbs.

The apples of both varieties are broad and flattened with a similar pinkish striped flush, but if seen together and it is possible to compare the two, the flush on Slack-ma-Girdle is a brighter red than that of Woodbine. Both varieties are ready at the same time in early November, but fruit will hang on the trees until January.

Fruit: Medium to large; 45–60mm. Oblate; often lop-sided; round with slight ribs. Stem a thick stub, within or projecting slightly from a narrow, deep cavity. Cavity of king fruits broad and shallow. Eye basin broad, deep, irregular, bumpy, tending to crowned; calyx usually open, sepals free. Skin pale green; smooth; lenticels often russeted dots. Always 50–80% flushed pinkish-mauve diffuse, distinctly striped or flecked bright red. Flesh sweet often with some astringency in the skin; pale greenish; chewy.

Juice: SG 1052; acidity 0.24%; tannin 0.14%

Cider: Slack-ma-Girdle cider is very rich and full bodied with a good aroma and flavor. It is pleasant alone although somewhat sweet, so is better blended with a brisker cider.

SOMERSET REDSTREAK

Early Bittersweet Cider Apple

Said to be a very old variety from the south east of the county, Somerset Redstreak shares some similar characteristics with the bittersharps from the Lambrook area, such as Lambrook Pippin and Porters Perfection. Unlike these, its fruits are a generous size, bittersweet and early. Somerset Redstreak may be less common in old standard orchards but it has been planted extensively since 1970s. It has proved to be a useful, if often rather biennial, reliable early harvesting variety and now occurs frequently in bush orchards in all the cider growing counties. The variety has gained sufficient recent popularity to be propagated as a standard tree for gapping-up old orchards.

Somerset Redstreak is predictably biennial in its cropping habit and makes a rather shapeless bush tree if left to its own devices. Trees are moderately vigorous with numerous primary lateral branches, but lack good centre leader dominance. In its exuberance it often over-crops so heavily that branches break under the strain, but such is its vitality that it constantly throws up new branches to replace the broken ones. Flowering is mid-season in early May. It is slightly susceptible to mildew, sawfly and brown rot but not scab.

The attractive shiny red apples are medium sized and conical. They mature early at the end of September and drop freely in early October, but the fallen fruits are quick to deteriorate if not collected promptly.

Fruit: Medium-large; 50–more than 60mm. Flattened conical, base rounded; regular; occasional fused fruits are produced. Stem thick, fleshy, within or occasionally projecting slightly from a medium sized, fairly deep cavity. Eye basin usually broad, deep and slightly bumpy; calyx usually more or less open; sepals short. Skin greenish-yellow; smooth, greasy or waxy, even sticky; russet is never more than slight in the stem cavity; lenticels inconspicuous. Always more than 75% flushed bright red, flecked and slightly striped darker red, spreading from eye but less round stem end. Flesh sweet with astringency; juicy; white; chewy.

Juice: SG 1050; acidity 0.19%; tannin 0.35%

Cider: Somerset Redstreak can make a pleasant single variety cider, medium bittersweet with soft tannin. It is often best when blended with some sharper varieties.

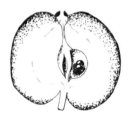

SOPS IN WINE

Sub-Acid Dual Purpose Apple

Synonyms: Sapson, Sapsovine etc. Possibly also Pendragon from Cornwall

Sops in Wine was described by Hogg as '*A very ancient [?17th Century] English culinary and cider apple, perhaps more singular than useful.*' Bunyard says in 1920, '*There are many red fleshed apples to which this name is applied . . . It is of no particular merit.*' However, it deserves a place here because it was at one time a common apple in West Country orchards and, at least in the 19th century, it undoubtedly made much cider. Trees are vigorous and spreading but it is said to be an excellent bearer.

The fruits of the 'true' Sops in Wine are quite rounded and covered in a dark crimson flush. The flesh is white stained with red as if soaked in wine. Apples should be ripe by early to mid October.

Fruit: Medium-large, 50 to more than 60mm. Rounded cylindrical, broad nose and rounded base; lopsided, tending to ribbed. Stem woody, within or projecting slightly from a small but deep cavity. Eye basin small, shallow even slight, tending to crowned; calyx open, sepals short. Skin yellow; smooth, waxy. Lenticels with pale surround. Some scab. Flush always present. Fruits often completely covered, dark red diffuse flush with slight stripes. Flesh tastes rather non-descript dessert, pleasantly sweet, very mildly sharp; melting texture, juicy. White, always with much reddening below skin and red vascular strands.

Juice: SG 1065; acidity 0.19%; tannin 0.13%

Cider: No cider-maker's comments found but this variety is unlikely to be useful on its own.

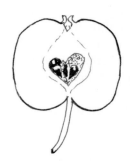

SPOTTED DICK

Late Bittersweet Cider Apple

Probably local to the Honiton area of Devon from where samples of fruit came to the Cider Institute in 1927–31. Old trees were still standing at Sowton Farm, Feniton Court in 1995 along with Green Sharp, White Sheep's Nose, Pound and Sour Clusters. The trees are fairly small with a neat head. It is now propagated and easily available, mostly for its interesting name and appearance, although it should make a good contribution to cider. Flowers mid May.

Fruits are small barrel shaped yellow-green distinctly spotty with corky lenticels that very often turn black. Ready late October-November

Fruit: Small-medium, 40–55mm. Barrel shaped cylindrical with a rounded base. Stem long and thin, projecting considerably from a slight, shallow cavity. Eye basin shallow and slightly puckered. Eye more or less open, sepals reflexed. Skin dull greenish turning to pale yellow when ripe. Lenticels distinctive, large, dark and corky dots. Flush absent. Flesh bittersweet with some acidity; greenish and melting.

Juice: SG 1051; acidity 0.25%; tannin 0.25%

Cider: Single sample made at the Institute in 1928 was described as '. . . *quite useful but lacking in body*.'

STABLE JERSEY

Late Full Bittersweet Cider Apple

This is a typical Somerset 'jersey' with a full bittersweet taste. Propagation material was brought to Long Ashton in 1987 for a clean-up and virus elimination. After that there were limited new plantings by Showerings Cider Company, but this variety is quite frequent in old orchards from Shepton Mallet to Glastonbury and down to the north of Dorset. It has been propagated more recently as standard trees but it has not been adopted for bush orchard planting although it does have some potential as a good late bittersweet that deserves a future. Trees are upright and spreading with rather unmanageable vigorous branches. It is said to be prone to canker. It is a tip-bearer and flowers in mid May.

The apples are bright red and gold striped, a rather waisted conical shape, and have a stub of a stem. They mature from mid October to early November.

Fruit: Medium to large 45–60mm. Conical, waisted; usually rounded with a trace of ribbing. Stem thick, fleshy stub, usually within or projecting slightly from a slight or narrow cavity. Eye basin small but well defined, sometimes bumpy and irregularly beaded; calyx closed or sometimes slightly open, sepals green at base. Skin pale golden yellow, slightly silvered; smooth, greasy; russet in stem cavity, occasional patches elsewhere. Always more than 75% often completely flushed, heavy, bright red, strongly striped dark crimson. Flesh full bittersweet; dry, chewy; greenish, browning rapidly.

Juice: SG 1058; acidity 0.25%; tannin 0.28%

Cider: Stable Jersey makes a full flavoured cider but with a very hard tannin character. Useful for blending and extending.

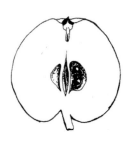

STEMBRIDGE CLUSTERS

Mid Season Sharp Cider Apple

Synonyms: Porter's Sheep's Nose, Sam Duck's Clusters and Cluster Jersey are possibly all the same variety

Stembridge Clusters is a typical 'jersey' to look at but unusually for a jersey, this one is a sharp with only a little tannin. It was most probably a protégé of Mr Sam Duck of Stembridge. Several old trees still stand in his orchard on Burrow Hill today. It was introduced for Taunton Cider in 1957, by the orcharding manager, John Stuckey of Stembridge, when it was almost certainly renamed Stembridge Clusters. In the 1970s it was widely planted in small quantities in bush orchards for Taunton

Cider, but it is not popular because of its disease susceptibility. It is very inclined to scab, canker and blossom wilt if left untreated. True to its name it carries its fruit in clusters of up to five and so has a strong tendency to crop biennially like many other old varieties. Bush trees are strong and spreading with much unruly vigour but moderate spurring develops with age. The variety flowers in late May and the apples are ready for harvest by mid to late October.

The apples are quite distinctive, rounded conical, yellow with scant but distinct bright red stripes and a long stem.

Fruit: Small-medium, 40–55mm. Conical, sometimes conical-cylindrical; rounded and regular. Stem woody, projecting distinctly from a slight cavity. Eye basin slight or small, often beaded or puckered; calyx open or closed, sepals upright, long. Skin greenish-yellow; smooth and dry. Flush usually about 30% but up to 65%; scant but distinct bright red stripes, a little orange diffuse flush but ground colour predominates. Flesh sharp with mild astringency; greenish; juicy and chewy.

Juice: SG 1050; acidity 0.50%; tannin 0.14%

Cider: This variety was introduced after testing had finished at Long Ashton but its taste suggests that it would make a pleasantly flavoured, slightly thin, sharp cider.

STEMBRIDGE JERSEY

Late Mid Season Bittersweet Cider Apple

This is a small Somerset 'jersey' apple, a useful bittersweet variety that first came to Long Ashton in 1947, sent in by Mr Stuckey of Stembridge, under the new name of Stembridge Jersey. It was submitted to the 1957 Long Ashton trials by his son John Stuckey, then Orchard Manager for Taunton Cider Company, and has subsequently found its way into many of the bush orchards that were planted to supply the Company in the 1970s. Stembridge Jersey makes a medium to large, spreading tree which is quick growing and early into cropping but soon becomes biennial. It has rather lost favour since it does tend to suffer from scab, severely on occasions and the apples are rather too small for machine harvesting. It flowers in mid May.

Stembridge Jersey are typical 'jersey' shape with bright red and green stripes. They mature from mid to late October but tend to drop over a long period as they ripen.

Fruit: Small-medium, 40–55mm. Flattened, rounded conical, rather shouldered; angular in section. Stem thick, fleshy, long, often strigged and offset, projecting distinctly from a small, deep cavity. Eye basin absent or slight, slightly beaded and furrowed; calyx closed, sepals short. Skin greenish yellow; smooth, dry. Lenticels often large and russeted with a pale surround. Scab susceptible. Usually a trace of flush, sometimes up to 50%, pinkish, slightly striped with dark crimson. Flesh medium bittersweet; greenish, browning rapidly, chewy.

Juice: SG 1052; acidity 0.18%; tannin 0.24–0.50%

Cider: This variety was introduced after cider trials had ceased at Long Ashton but its taste suggests that it would make a fair quality bittersweet cider with a typical Somerset character.

STOKE RED

Late Bittersharp Cider Apple

Synonyms: Neverblight, Stoke Redstripe

Raised and named Stoke Red by Herbert Harry Sealey of Rodney Stoke in Somerset, probably around the turn of the 20th century. From 1930 on, it was commonly included in trial orchards in all the cider growing counties, but it is more frequently found in Somerset. It is one of the parents of the briefly popular early variety, Ashton Bitter. Unfortunately Stoke Red has a poor natural tree shape. As a standard tree it is medium sized with a compact head formed of numerous small, thick, twiggy branches. On a dwarfing rootstock it forms a neat bush with numerous branches but no centre leader. It is still fairly resistant to scab and mildew. Even as a bush it is slow to come into cropping and will invariably become biennial, but its crops are good. Flowering time is late May. Although Stoke Red makes excellent cider, the small size of its fruit which matures fairly late towards the 3rd week November and its poor tree habit, makes it an unpopular choice for bush orchards.

The apples are quite easy to identify; small, flattened spherical and all over striped dark red.

Fruit: Small; less than 40–45mm. Flattened spherical, rarely flattened conical; regular. Stem variable, within cavity or projecting slightly from a slight or shallow stem cavity. Eye basin well defined, shallow, sometimes deep, regular, smooth, sometimes pubescent at the base; calyx closed, sepals very pubescent. Skin yellow or greenish-yellow; smooth; slightly waxy; little scab; russet usually only in stem cavity; lenticels usually inconspicuous. Usually more than 75%, frequently completely flushed and striped dark red. Flesh sharp usually with some astringency; white, sometimes slightly reddened; soft, very juicy.

Juice: SG 1052; acidity 0.64%; tannin 0.31%. Often scented and pink.

Cider: Stoke Red can produce an excellent, balanced, bittersharp juice which makes a very good, distinguished single variety cider with a pleasant fruity aroma, second only to Kingston Black and sometimes preferred. Fermentation can be slow.

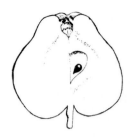

STUBBARD

Very Early Dual Purpose Apple

Synonyms: Michaelmas Stubbard, Summer Stibbert, Summer Queening

This is a very old, possibly 16th century kitchen apple, ready early August and sometimes used for making a first early cider. The RHS Journal records it from 1805 onwards. It is a pitcher whose antiquity is verified by its ability to root from cuttings. It is recorded as *'A Devonshire apple, an early and popular apple for August with a distinctive flavour.'* and is described by Hogg in his Fruit Manual 1884 as *'An early kitchen apple which comes into use in the middle and end of August . . . a very popular apple in the West of England especially in Cornwall, Devon and Somerset.'* We have found it quite often in West Dorset. Our young trees in the nursery were tall and very vigorous with plenty of good feathers [Distributed 2011]. Older mature trees are strong and spreading.

It is a variety that is described under many of its names in many other records and remains an attractive Wessex curiosity worth keeping.

Stubbard fruits are unmistakeable; large and knobbly lemon yellow with a pinched and furrowed nose. Ready very early.

Fruit: Medium to large, 50–>60 mm. Rounded cylindrical with a pinched nose and small rounded base; heavily ribbed from base to apex, irregular, angular and often lop-sided. Stem thick, fleshy, often strigged, projecting distinctly from a narrow deep cavity. Eye basin slight, shallow, irregular, furrowed and often beaded, sepals reflexed, green. Eye open, or closed if sepals intact. Skin smooth, dry with a few large russet dots. Pale yellow ripening to butter yellow. No flush or very slight blush of pinkish-brown. Core very large, open; tube a broad cone often extending deeply toward the core. Flesh distinctive flavour, sharp; white or yellowish; melting and juicy.

Juice: SG 1043; acidity 0.83%; tannin 0.17%

Cider: No cidermakers records found. As a very early maturing apple, Stubbard might be included in the first-early cider made in the season, when it would contribute useful flavour and some sugar.

Our Stubbard cider sample made in 2007 was rated as 'Rather woody tasting, sharp cider, lacking body but would be good for blending.'

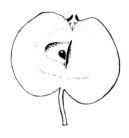

SWEET ALFORD

Late Sweet Cider Apple

A well known and widely planted variety said to have originated in Devon, where it has a reputation for good cropping. But it may be a Somerset apple since it occurs in the south of the county and also in north Dorset as old trees. Standard trees are large to very large, upright with a full spreading, thickly spurred head. It is a tip-bearer with characteristic forked twigs. Cropping is good but the fruit seems to be very susceptible to scab. Many bush trees that pass under the name, Sweet Alford, planted in the 1970s, are in fact another variety called Le Bret. A mix-up that may have occurred during propagation at Long Ashton for the virus-free mother tree orchard.

Sweet Alford fruits have a waxy yellow skin often with a diffuse flush associated with damage or bruising. They are distinguished from Le Bret by their smaller size and by their long, thin stems. This variety flowers in mid May and the fruit matures in the first part of November.

Fruit: Medium, 45–55mm. Flattened conical. Stem thin, woody; projecting considerably from a pronounced, deep cavity. Eye basin shallow, puckered; calyx slightly open, sepals large, reflexed, upright. Skin yellow, sometimes greenish-yellow; smooth, waxy; russet sometimes a thin network; scab susceptible, slight mildew. Flush frequent but covering less than a third with slight diffuse pink-orange. Flesh sweet, little or no astringency; white, slightly crisp.

Juice: SG 1052; acidity 0.20%; tannin 0.18%

Cider: Good quality, sweet, soft and fruity, often with a suggestion of tannin.

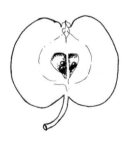

SWEET BAY

Bittersweet Cider Apple

A Devon bittersweet from the Crediton area. Possibly also good as an eating apple.
Flowering mid season.

A medium sized uninspiring looking, rounded green apple with a long stem. Ready October.

Fruit: Size varies according to the crop. 40–55mm. Flattened conical with a small flat nose and a rounded base. Stem long and protruding distinctly, 15mm, from a narrow, deep, smooth cavity. Eye basin small, narrow and rather puckered. Eye more or less closed. Skin greenish-yellow to yellow, smooth, sometimes partly flushed orangey-yellow with a few carmine flecks and russet dots.

Juice: SG 1050; acidity 0.49%; tannin 0.23%

Cider: Sadly no cidermaker's notes.

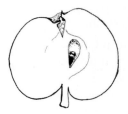

SWEET CLEAVE

Sweet to Sub-Acid Dual Purpose

Synonym: Flanders Pippin

Often reported to have come from Berkshire but strongly claimed by Barnstable as a local variety dating back to the early 19th century in use for both eating and cidermaking then as now. The fruits are typical knobbly, and large, similar to many other West Country dual purpose apples. This variety claims very good resistance to scab. [Some scab on our samples] It flowers quite early in May or late April.

The large, brownish-red striped knobbly apples are ready by the end of September.

Fruit: Large 55–>60mm. Broadly conical; strongly ribbed, angular, rather 5 sided. Stem quite short [5–10mm] within or projecting slightly from a large, deep, gold russeted cavity. Eye basin small, narrow and deep, 5 or more crowned and furrowed. Eye slightly open, sepals upright. Skin yellow-green, smooth, slightly waxy. Occasional russet patches and dots. Always well covered with a brownish light flush, often a heavier dark red over the base with strong short stripes. Flesh sub-acid; dry, yellowish-green.

Juice: Mildly acidic.

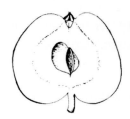

SWEET COPPIN

Late Mid Season Sweet Cider Apple

An old Devon variety, originally from the Exeter area and found throughout Somerset and west Dorset as old trees. The name Coppin derives from the wooden spools used to wind thread in cloth factories. More recently it has been propagated as standard trees and has now found its way into many renovated orchards, but it is only rarely used as a bush tree. Mature trees are fairly easy to recognise, both standard and bush, from the large, rounded head of thin whippy, twiggy, thickly spurred growth. In the dormant season, the bark on current year's shoot growth has a distinctive golden sheen. As bush trees Sweet Coppin can crop quite regularly when persuaded to, but fruit is late to mature, ready towards the end of October and into November. Flowering time is mid season. Rather susceptible to mildew, woolly aphid and scab in middle age.

The apples are basically conical in shape and frequently large on lightly cropping trees, but there are often many king fruits which are much more cylindrical. The skin is a pale yellow usually with a patch of orange, or mauveish flush.

Fruit: Medium, often large, 50–more than 60mm. Basically conical but variable, sometimes flattened spherical; regular; king fruits cylindrical often irregular. Stem woody, usually projecting slightly from a wide, shallow cavity. Eye basin well defined, wide, shallow, smooth; calyx slightly open, sepals narrow, often free. Skin yellow to greenish-yellow; dry; russet usually light, sometimes spreading as network on cheek. Lenticels conspicuous, sometimes large and irregular, some surrounded by a small circle of red, lenticel spot common. Usually just a patch of diffuse orange-pink flush, occasionally flecked red. Flesh sweet with no astringency; white, soft.

Juice: SG 1052; acidity 0.20%; tannin 0.14%

Cider: Pure sweet, occasionally very mild bittersweet.

TALE SWEET

Late Mild Bittersweet Cider Apple

An east Devon variety introduced by H Daniels of Higher Tale Farm, Payhembury near Honiton around 1930, when cider was made on the farm for the London market. Later fruit was supplied to Whiteways cider factory in Whimple but the orchards were grubbed in the late 'fifties. Old trees may still exist [including another selection, Tale Sharp] in the Tale locality. Its trees are not easy to manage being rather weak and branching, but well spurred. Crops can be biennial. Flowers early May.

Tale Sweet apples mature slowly and ripen from a brownish-green flush to a more healthy looking maroon to be ready in November.

Fruit: Medium to large, 45–60mm. Flattened conical or oblate, somewhat angular. Stem thick, fleshy, projecting slightly, occasionally longer. Stem cavity small and deep. Eye basin medium, shallow and smooth. Sepals green, upright and free. Skin smooth, dry, whitish-green. Often russet cracks around the eye spread into patches of russet on the cheeks. Usually almost half covered with a distinctive, strongly speckled, dark maroon flush with a brownish-green mottle, lightening as it ripens. Flesh sweet, chewy, greenish with green vascular strands.

Juice: SG 1057; acidity 0.31%; tannin 0.16%

Cider: Reported as best in the sweet group in its first trial in 1930. Judges comment *'Could make a first class sweet.'*

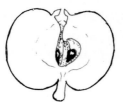

TEIGN HARVEY

Late Mid-season Bittersharp Cider Apple

Synonyms, Tan, Tin or Ting Harvey

The South Hams are the home of this apple. Records for cidermaking in the early part of 20th Century come from around Totnes, and there is a place named Teign Harvey in the Teign Estuary. It may well still be found from Teignmouth ['Tinmouth'] round through south Hams as far as the Tamar Valley and it is now propagated by several nurseries. Trees are moderately vigorous, spreading with sparse laterals. It is a good, reliable, heavy cropping variety but scab susceptible. Flowers, bold pink, at the end April-early May.

A small rounded, oblate apple, regular and smooth with a pinkish flush. Ready mid-late October

Fruit: Medium size, 40–55mm. Flattened conical with gently rounded ribs and a rounded nose and base. King fruits are more cylindrical. Stem thick and fleshy, especially in king fruit, usually a stub within the deep stem cavity, occasionally projecting slightly. Eye basin pronounced, narrow but deep, smooth and broadly furrowed. Eye usually closed and sepals reflexed. Skin pale yellow, usually up to half the fruit flushed orangey-pink, sometimes a few mauve spots. Skin smooth, dry becoming greasy, with slight netted russet around the eye sometimes spreading over the flush. Flesh mild bittersharp; white, juicy, melting or chewy.

Juice: SG 1052; acidity 0.45%; tannin 0.28%

Cider: Sweet, medium brisk. A fair quality but lacks body.

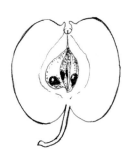

TANGY

Full Sharp Cider Apple

Preliminary name Moens Farm Tangy

An unknown apple tree was found growing in the hedge outside the farm gate in Loders near Bridport in West Dorset during our DATA Project search for lost Dorset cider apples. This one is most probably a seedling but its remarkable citric taste could make it a useful choice to balance a sweet blend. The tree had been pruned hard through regular hedge trimming but was still able to produce a good crop of apples. Our trees in the nursery were strong, upright and free branching. They had a good shape and plentiful feathers and should do well.[Distributed 2011]

Tangy is ready early mid season, late September-early October. A Very sharp tasting small, almost elliptical pale golden apple with a long stem. Similar to a wild apple, *Malus sylvestris* but ripening to a clear golden yellow. The genuine wild apples remain green and have a very astringent taste.

Fruit: Small-medium, 40–55 mm. Elliptical with a small rounded base; rounded with a trace of ribs. Stem long [>25mm], thin, green, projecting considerably from a narrow, deep cavity. Eye basin slight, crowned, tending to beaded; calyx usually open, sepals green, broken. Skin smooth, waxy, without russet. Yellow-green ripening to pale gold. No flush. Flesh full citric sharp taste; chewy, greenish.

Juice: Very sharp, almost citric. SG 1051, sugar 12.5%

Cider: Unlikely to make a drinkable cider on its own but could be useful blended to give a clean, sharp tang to a mediocre sweet or bittersweet cider.

TAYLORS

Mid Season Sweet Cider Apple

Synonym: Taylor's Sweet, Taylor's Seedling

This old variety, sometime incorrectly called Taylor's Bitter, was originally propagated at Porter's Nursery near South Petherton, in the late 19th Century. Although it is a sweet apple with little tannin in the juice, it was planted in many new bush cider orchards throughout the counties to act as a pollinator for the more valued, early flowering variety, Tremlett's Bitter. Taylor's Sweet is a true tip bearer. Each fruit cluster produces two shoots which in turn produce two others. Because of this curious dichotomous branching habit, it forms a distinctive weeping tree. It is quite vigorous but produces few useful primary branches. As a bush tree it is difficult to maintain a good centre leader and spurring is very poor. It is not precocious and will slowly go biennial. Leaves of this variety are distinctively grey, with a pale underside. Flowering time is late April, early May when the cream coloured blossom is particularly attractive.

The apples which are often held in multiple clusters, are tall and distinctly but sparsely striped red and green. They fall early to mid October and are fairly firm.

Fruit: Large, 55–60mm. Cylindrical tending to conical; oval in cross section. Stem woody, projecting distinctly; cavity medium, narrow and deep. Eye basin slight, shallow, irregular; calyx often open, sepals reflexed, long. Skin pale yellow-green; smooth, dry; russet often in stem cavity. Always 30% flush or less, light red diffuse, strongly flecked and striped crimson. Flesh sweet; chewy, firm; white, browning rapidly.

Juice: SG 1053; acidity 0.18%; tannin 0.15%. Pure sweet.

Cider: Taylor's Seedling produces a light to medium cider with good flavour and aroma but rather coarse, lacking character and quality. Useful for blending.

TEN COMMANDMENTS

Dual Purpose Sub-Acid Apple

Synonym: Said to be same as Reinette Rouge Étoilée

This well known apple frequently occurs in farm orchards throughout the West Country and also in Hereford. It gets its name from the reddened vascular strands in the flesh which show up as ten red spots when the fruit is cut in half. Sometimes, in fruit from old orchards these vascular strands are not coloured, especially if the trees are overgrown and the orchard is dark so that the fruit gets little sunlight. There seem to be many descriptions and many variations of this variety, some of them possibly just look-alike seedlings, that go under the same name. Ten Commandments is a dual purpose apple, sub-acid, useful for eating, cooking or putting in with the ciderapples. Trees are moderately vigorous. Their blossom is attractive in early May.

True Ten Commandments are eye-catching beetroot red apples with conspicuous light coloured dots. Ready for harvest in early October.

Fruit: Medium; 45–55mm. Rather oblate or flattened conical; rounded tending to angular. Stem a short thick stub within a small but fairly deep cavity. Eye basin medium, smooth and regular; eye wide open, sepals often short. Skin yellow, smooth, dry or slightly waxy with age. Russet usually confined to stem cavity.

Lenticels very conspicuous, large, russeted. Flush often complete. Strongly diffuse and slightly striped with dark, beetroot red, sometimes slightly striped bright red. Flesh sharp, sub-acid; melting; white, reddened under the skin, often with red vascular strands.

Juice: SG 1055; acidity 0.18%; tannin 0.13%; Nitrogen 15.2mg/100mg
[NB. The average is 5–10mg/100mg]

Cider: Ten Commandments is unlikely to make a good cider alone, but the pink juice, skin and flesh might just give a pink tint if there was a sufficient quantity of them in the blend. Best blended with bittersweet varieties. Nitrogen may be high in some samples and fermentation will be accelerated.

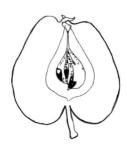

TOM LEGG

Mid Season Mild Bittersweet Cider Apple

Two trees of this traditional Dorset variety rediscovered during the DATA Project search for lost Dorset cider apples, were first found in a small farm orchard near Shaves Cross in West Dorset. The apples, similar to the variety Belle Norman, fit the description of Tom Legg as in the list of local varieties in 1939 but little is known about them other than that. The two trees remaining on the farm were medium sized with a compact head and still cropping well.

Ready mid October, the pale greenish-yellow fruits are tall, waisted conical in shape and have a good flavour. If this is the true variety, it should make a good contribution to the flavour of local ciders.

Fruit: Medium, 45–55mm. Tall conical, rather waisted with a long, narrow nose and a small rounded base; 10 well rounded ribs in section. Stem projects distinctly from a narrow cavity. [10–15mm]. Eye basin small, crowned and irregular. Eye usually closed, sepals short. Skin dry. Occasional russet dots. Yellow-green to pale greenish-yellow. Flesh mild bittersweet, chewy and yellowish.

Juice: Astringent, full, fruity aroma.
SG 1045; acidity 0.21%; tannin 0.25%

TOMMY KNIGHT

Late Sub-acid Apple used for Cider

A Cornish cider apple from St Agnes district that it was first exhibited in 1861. Rediscovered by James Evans and Mary Martin in 1981 from St Agnes and later at St Dominick, Trebullet and Gunnislake. Found in Cornwall and neighbouring Devon, this variety is best used as a late to very late season cider apple, although it can also be a quite pleasant dessert apple. Mature trees are moderately vigorous. Young trees are dense and whippy which, as the tree matures, forms a mass of small twigs, making it compact and similar in appearance to a thorn bush. Flowers early May.

The apples are smallish, bright red and rather flattened with green russet around the stem. Ready late October.

Fruit: Small-medium 40–55mm. Flattened conical or cylindrical. Round in section, faintly ribbed. Stem thick, fleshy [10mm], either within or projecting slightly from a medium size cavity lined with green-gold russet. Eye usually slightly open with long green sepals, in a narrow basin with five distinct knobbly crowns. Skin pale yellow-green, rather rough but waxy, usually more than half covered in a bright scarlet flush with strong dark red streaks and stripes. Greenish russet streaks often spreading from stem to eye. Flesh greenish, hard, crisp and juicy. Core small, closed with a broad conical tube.

Juice: Sharp and sweet with a good dessert flavour.

Cider: No records.

TOM PUTT

Early Dual Purpose Cider Apple

Synonyms: Coalbrook, Marrowbone, Ploughman and many others

Tom Putt is an 18th century variety. It is arguable whether it is a native of Devon, Dorset or of Somerset, since it was either raised by Rev Thomas Putt [1757–1844], rector of Trent, which is now in Dorset but was formerly in Somerset, or by his uncle, Tom Putt who lived near Honiton in Devon. It may have been he who brought it to his nephew's garden in Trent. It is still widely distributed as a dual purpose apple all over the West Country. Always popular for gardens and home orchards, it is sometimes referred to as the Cottage Apple. Tom Putt has been quoted as *'A rosy apple that grew in every garden and every orchard.'*

Tom Putt trees are vigorous and spreading. They have remarkable powers of rejuvenation even in old age, often throwing out new, vigorous branches from the base or even from the remains of a stump. As a variety it has now become rather variable. There are also Red and White Tom Putts, which are similar in all other respects. It is an early flowering variety and because of this, seems to be prone to apple sawfly. Apples begin to drop in August, often because of codling moth which also seem to trouble them, and tend to rot quickly.

Tom Putt fruits are full of character, broadly conical, rather knobbly and irregular, and more or less covered with a striped and flecked, bright red flush.

Fruit: Large; 55–more than 60mm. Flattened conical, broad base, narrow nose; strongly ribbed, irregular. Stem short, within or protruding slightly from a medium, narrow cavity. Eye basin deep, ribbed or crowned, irregular; calyx open, sepals short, upright. Skin greenish yellow; shiny, waxy; very little russet; scab susceptible. Flush rather variable, always more than 75%, distinctly striped and flecked, bright crimson over red diffuse. Red Tom Putt, a sport with heavy red diffuse flush and no stripes. Flesh sub acid; soft; yellowish and tastes good cooked.

Juice: SG 1052; acidity 0.65%; tannin 0.13%

Cider: Tom Putt, a typical dual purpose apple, is a mild sharp and makes a somewhat thin, dry and sharp cider. But its flavour is clean and pleasant and it usually improves after keeping a while.

TOM TANNERS
Late Full Bittersharp Cider Apple

Also DATA Project preliminary names Dashayes Red and Marnhull Bitters

This variety was first recorded at Long Ashton, sent from Butleigh in mid Somerset as a full bittersharp. It was later planted in some trials orchards and was included the now extinct Whettons Museum orchard at Broxwood, Herefordshire. It may have been the Tanners Red described by Hogg in his *The Apple and Pear as Vintage Fruits* 1886 as '*An apple without any known history.*' During the first half of the 20th century Tom Tanners was a well known variety for cider making in Rodney Stoke, near Wells, Somerset [pers.com] where it had a reputation for its intense tannin and high sugar content. It was found again recently in several old orchards on the north Dorset, south Somerset border. Tanners trees are usually fairly small and scab susceptible. Our young trees in the nursery were short and stout with few feathers. In 2011, before their identity was confirmed, they were distributed under both provisional names and not as Tom Tanners. Hopefully they are all now correctly named. Flowering early mid-season.

Tom Tanners apples are conical and slightly waisted, with a shiny crimson, heavy dark red striped flush and prominent lenticels. They are ready mid-late October.

Fruit: Small-medium large, 45–60mm. Conical, slightly waisted or nosed, base rounded; round in section and sometimes slightly ribbed. Stem fairly short [5–10mm], projecting slightly from a small, narrow and deep, green russeted cavity. Eye basin small and shallow, irregular and often slightly beaded. Eye more or less open, sepals long, upright and often green. Skin smooth, dry and shiny. Can be roughened by scab. Sometimes with a network of golden russet. Lenticels large, frequently with a pale surround especially on the flush and on the base. Colour pale yellow-green always more than half, sometimes completely covered with a heavy dark red flush, slightly striped and flecked. Flesh bittersharp with heavy tannin. Greenish, often reddened below the skin on the nose. Tube often open to the core.

Juice: SG often high, >1060; acidity 0.30%; tannin 0.60–0.90%. Pale pink in colour.

Cider: No cider makers notes found but this variety must be the ultimate extender!

TREMLETT'S BITTER

Early Bittersweet Cider Apple

Synonym: Trimmies in parts of Devon. Might also be found incorrectly named Whimple Early

A popular Devon variety which is commonly found throughout all the cider growing counties in bush and standard orchards, many planted since the 1950s. Although very biennial in its cropping, Tremlett's can produce huge crops of smallish fruit. It is a useful early variety, maturing in the first half of October. It has the disadvantage of flowering very early, often in late April, when it is at risk of being caught by late frosts. Although self-sterile and needing a pollinator such as Taylor's Seedling, it is a useful pollinator for other early varieties. Mature standard trees are slow to come in to crop, medium sized with a spreading habit. Bush trees are somewhat difficult to manage, being full of vigour they tend to throw out heavily spurred branches in all directions, forming a dense mass around the centre leader. It is a very scab susceptible variety and a bad infection can cause the leaves to drop prematurely.

The elongated conical apples mature in late September. A Tremlett's Bitter tree full of strikingly bright red shiny ripe fruit is a picture.

Fruit: Medium, 45–55mm. Conical tending to cylindrical; base round, nose pointed. Stem woody, usually projecting slightly from a small, shallow cavity. Eye basin small, calyx tightly closed, sepals long and reflexed, pubescent. Skin yellow, sometimes greenish; smooth and waxy. Lenticels conspicuous, usually small but surrounded by a light patch. Scab susceptible. Always more than two thirds, often completely flushed, bright mid red, slightly striped. Flesh sweet and astringent; white, woolly.

Juice: SG 1052; acidity 0.27%; tannin 0.34%

Cider: Full bittersweet, hard and bitter tannin. Can taste slightly mousey.

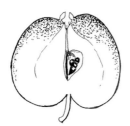

TWENTY PIP

Early Mild Bittersharp Dual Purpose Apple

During Long Ashton's search for September maturing cider apples in the early 1980s, a single tree was found in an orchard in Clyst Honiton near Exeter. As its identity was never discovered, it was named 20 Pip, since many of the fruits had twice the full compliment of seeds. It could possibly be a seedling of Worcester Pearmain but lacks the distinctive aroma and flavour. Twenty Pip was never propagated for commercial use but it may be found occasionally in fairly recent plantings. Trees have moderate vigour and make a compact head, are disease free and regular cropping. Flowers early with Tremletts Bitter.

The good looking apples are more than half covered with a distinctly striped crimson flush. Ready end of September.

Fruit: Medium to large 50–>60mm. Conical with a pointed nose and round base; regular. Stem slender, woody, occasionally red in some fruits. Usually long and projecting considerably from a medium sized, deep cavity. Eye basin small and narrow, crowned and bumpy. Eye open, sepals free, long, large and green. Skin pale yellow green, almost covered with heavy bright red flush, distinctly striped a darker red. Lenticels often show as pale brown dots. Flesh yellowish, reddened under the skin, juicy and melting.

Juice: Sub-acid with slight tannin mostly in the skin.

Cider: 1985 sample described as '. . . *rather 'woody' with little tannin*.'

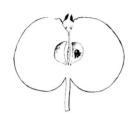

VALLIS APPLE

Mid Season Sharp Cider Apple

Synonyms: Black or Red Vallis, Redskins

Although this variety looks similar to the true Kingston Black, it comes nowhere near the legendary 'KB' flavour and vintage quality. Vallis is a pure sharp with little tannin and is probably more closely related to Improved Kingston Black. It is often familiarly known as Redskins in the north of Somerset where it originated. This shiny red apple was attractive and palatable enough to be sold for an eating apple in Bristol Market at one time. Its red tinged flesh would have been attractive in the days when there were few apples of distinction for sale to the general public. There are some variations in trees from different districts but in general they are large, even very large, upright and spreading, with a full head of dark green leaves. Red and Black Vallis are probably distinct clones of the variety with fruit varying in colour from scarlet to almost black. Vallis is described as a good cropper but may to be susceptible to sawfly. Flowering time is mid to late May.

Vallis apples are ready from mid to late October. They are usually round and regular, distinctly flattened like a top and more or less covered in a strong red flush.

Fruit: Medium to large; 50–more than 60mm. Variable shape, usually oblate, base and nose broad, sometimes more conical tending to waisted; basically regular but often lopsided, tending to angular. Stem thin, woody, projecting distinctly from a large, broad, deep cavity. Eye basin medium, narrow, deep, furrowed or irregular, crowned or slightly beaded; calyx usually closed, sepals upright, long, broad, free. Skin smooth, greasy, very shiny; slight scab. Skin yellow to yellow-green, always more than 75%, often almost completely flushed strong, bright cherry red to bright red diffuse, occasional patches almost black. Flesh sharp, sweet, dessert taste and texture; juicy, melting; greenish, often tinged with red under the skin.

Juice: Sub-acid. SG 1056; acidity 0.70%; tannin 0.15%

Cider: Vallis was reported to make a pleasant, clean tasting but not outstanding cider. Fermentation may be rather rapid.

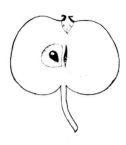

VILBERIE

Late Full Bittersweet Cider Apple

This is a French variety introduced by H P Bulmer in the late 19th Century. It is seldom found as old standard trees in the South West, but does occur as youngish replacement trees, and also in a few bush orchards planted for Showering's and Taunton Cider companies in the early 1970s. It is normally found in association with Brown Snout, another late flowering and maturing variety, both chosen to fill low lying, frosty spots in orchards. Vilberie trees are very vigorous, open and horizontally spreading, so much so that it is difficult to maintain a good centre leader since it tends to go over to the leeward side. Cropping is heavy but biennial. It is susceptible to leaf mildew and frequently gets fireblight because of its late flowering habit.

Vilberie apples are rather flattened conical and green with a dull, brownish flush. Although they are not ready to harvest until well into November, they weigh heavily.

Fruit: Medium, 45–55mm. Flattened conical; regular or slightly angular. Stem long, usually projecting considerably from a narrow cavity. Eye basin small, puckered; calyx slightly open, sepals long and reflexed. Skin waxy. Russet slight in stem cavity, occasionally spreading in patches. Skin dark green, usually with a brownish-red diffuse flush spreading from the eye over one-two thirds. Flesh full bittersweet; greenish; chewy, hard.

Juice: SG 1062; acidity 0.23%; tannin 0.50%

Cider: Sweet with full astringency; good quality.

WARRIOR

Early Mid-season Bittersharp

Synonyms: Possibly the original Yellow Redstreak.
Preliminary DATA Project name, Joanies

Warrior is clearly a popular variety in Dorset. Many similar trees can be seen from Bridport in the west, through to Cattistock and on up to the Somerset- North Dorset border. But the only record of the name Warrior, is to be found in the National Apple Register, brought to an RHS exhibition in 1947. However, it is possible that it is actually the very old variety, Yellow Redstreak, as described by Hogg in *'The Apple and Pear as Vintage Fruits'* in 1886. A tree, identified as Yellow Redstreak was found in an old orchard in Stembridge, Somerset in 1964 and was propagated

Angela

Fiona

Gilly

Hastings

Helens Apple

Lizzy

Prince William

Three Counties

Vicky

Willy

Amanda

Amelia

Bush tree Hastings

Connie

Shamrock

Tracey

Jane

Margaret

Sally

Tina

Joanna

Hannah

Jenny

Naomi

Nicky

Betty

Eleni

Debbie

Early Bird

Jean

at Long Ashton in modest numbers for trials. All the Warrior samples that we have seen match the description of these Yellow Redstreaks. If we accept the change of name we have a cider variety that was highly regarded by Hogg and very worthy of its place in cidermaking today. '*A high sugar variety valuable for mixing with other more astringent varieties for cider making.*' '*The tree is hardy and grows to a good size and bears freely*'.

The trees are moderately vigorous, upright with a large spreading head. Cropping tends to be rather biennial. Our young trees in the nursery were short, stout and compact [Distributed 2013 as Warrior or Joanie]. Their very large rounded leaves with broad crenulated margins were characteristically down-curled.

The tall, handsome shiny apples with their distinctive irregularly furrowed and crowned noses are strongly striped bright red over golden yellow. Maturing early-mid October.

Fruit: Fairly large, 50–60mm. Flattened conical, often tall and slightly waisted, base rounded; often very lopsided, gently ribbed. Stem usually projecting distinctly [<10mm] from a deep cavity. Eye basin small and narrow, crowned and furrowed, sometimes beaded. Eye usually open, sepals upright, long, green. Skin shiny, waxy or greasy; only occasionally a little russet. Colour yellow green to bright golden yellow, usually at least half strongly flecked and striped bright red over diffuse orange. Core large, open; tube a broad U-shape or cone. Flesh sharp or bittersharp, juicy, melting or slightly chewy, cream; some bitterness in the skin.

Juice: Sharp with slight hint of tannin, sweet aroma.
SG 1.050; malic acid 0.88%; tannin 0.33g/l

Cider: Our DATA ciders 2007.
Sample 1] Pale amber, fresh, slightly citric. Well balanced acidity and astringency. Good slightly sweetened or blended.

Sample 2] Piquant slightly smoky pale straw coloured with a marked apple taste. But mouth-wateringly acidic with some astringency. Suitable only for blending.

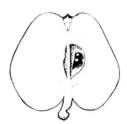

WEAR AND TEAR

Mid Season Dual Purpose Cider Apple
Synonyms: Glastonbury Wear and Tear, Bear and Tear
There are still odd trees of Wear and Tear standing in old orchards round the Glastonbury area where it originated, even one or two on the Tor itself. It is aptly named from its habit of breaking under the weight of heavy crops, but it has the remarkable ability to rejuvenate itself, producing

strong new limbs even in old age. This variety was first recorded in 1883, but it is probably very old. Trees are tall, upright and spread with maturity. Some old trees are now showing signs of virus infection and their fruit is cracked and scarred and useless.

The apples are quite elongated conical with an irregular eye. The fruit stems are often distinctive, bulging and knobbly, and sometimes coloured pink. Mature by mid October to early November.

Fruit: Medium; 45–55mm. Elongated conical with a broad base. Stem thick, woody, usually with a bulge at the fruit end, projecting slightly, occasionally distinctly, sometimes coloured pink when flush is in stem cavity; king fruits with very thick, fleshy stems; stem cavity medium, conical, slightly ribbed. Eye basin fairly deep, very puckered, ribbed; usually irregular through scab; calyx closed, sepals touching, overlapping, fairly long, reflexed at tips. Skin smooth, slightly waxy, often disfigured with scab and virus infection. Lenticels conspicuous in bruises on ripe fruit. Very scab susceptible. Skin yellowish green, usually over half covered with a diffuse pink flush, speckled and flecked bright red; sometimes flushed pinkish in stem cavity. Flesh heavily sweet; white, dry; very soft dessert texture.

Juice: Heavy sweet, sub-acid.

Cider: No comments recorded but should make a rather thin sweet cider, so is probably best blended with other varieties with more character.

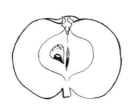

WHITE ALPHINGTON
Late Mid-season Sweet Cider Apple

Synonyms Loram's Spotted White, Sweet Alphington

This variety came from Mr Loram, a cidermaker of Alphington, now a built-up area south of Exeter, before 1900. It may still be infrequently found as old trees in the Exeter area and Exe valley. Some are still growing in the old Whiteways orchards in Whimple. It is a vigorous variety that rapidly makes a large, upright tree It crops prolifically but is very susceptible to fruit scab, hence it is aka, Spotted White. Flowers mid to late May.

The fruits, which are rather small, very pale yellow, almost white, are often very spotty. Ready mid-late October.

Fruit: Small to medium, 40–50mm. Flattened conical, base broad, round and nose small. Stem stout and fleshy, projecting slightly or within a narrow, deep cavity lined with pale green gold russet. Eye basin small, often irregular with scab. Sepals slightly open, green and reflexed at the tips. Skin very pale yellow, almost white. Occasional streaks and patches of russet on the cheeks . Scab susceptible and skin spotty. Sometimes flecked with a light scarlet flush. Flesh sweet with a hint of bitterness.

Juice: SG 1065; acidity 0.30%; tannin 0.15%
Often with a useful high sugar content.

Cider: Medium sweet with a pleasant aroma and taste. Fermentation moderate. Useful for blending but inclined to coarseness in flavour.

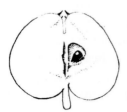

WHITE CLOSE PIPPIN
Medium Bittersweet Cider Apple
Synonym: Dry Close

White Close Pippin is scarce in its native county of Somerset. Although mentioned at the Bath and West Show in 1898, the earliest records at Long Ashton were of fruit sent from Sutton Montis in 1907. It clearly has good vintage qualities. Standard trees might still be found only very occasionally, often in some experimental bush orchards that were planted in the 1930s. There is a single remaining tree in the Axbridge Long Ashton trial orchard at Christon in Somerset. White Close forms a medium sized, quite vigorous tree with a spreading habit. It is free spurring and has been described as forming a 'thistle top' head, with its pale, whitish foliage. Cropping is variable, sometimes heavy. The fruit is rather susceptible to scab but said to have a good rich flavour and be good for jam making. Flowering time is mid season in May.

The apples are pale green, almost white or creamy with a rosy flush but sometimes heavily cracked and russeted. Maturing from mid October to November .

Fruit: Medium; 55–60mm. Conical, nose flat; rather irregular; king fruit slightly elongated. Stem level with base, more usually projecting slightly or considerably from a broad, deep cavity. Eye basin small, smooth or slightly puckered; calyx more or less open or wide open, sepals upright, rather pubescent. Skin smooth, dry; russet often spreading from stem cavity and nose, frequently net-like on cheek. Lenticels a distinctive feature, prominent, surrounded by a green patch on immature fruit, often russeted. Sometimes heavily cracked with scab. Colour very pale greenish white or cream., usually flushed 25–50% diffuse, slightly flecked or striped, rather pinkish-orange. Flesh medium or mild bittersweet, tannin in skin; pale yellow; chewy texture.

Juice: SG 1050; acidity 0.18%; tannin 0.24%

Cider: White Close Pippin makes a rich and fruity cider with an excellent flavour and aroma. The tannin is mild, so it can be good alone or blended. Sugar content is often above average but fermentation is inclined to be slow.

WHITE JERSEY

Early Bittersweet Cider Apple

Still widely distributed in old farm orchards in south Somerset, White Jersey was popular as a cider apple in the 19th century, and was listed by Lloyd for the Bath and West Society in 1895. More recently it was considered to have some promise as an early maturing variety for bush orchards. In the mid 1980s, there were limited plantings although it has not enjoyed quite the same popularity as other early maturing varieties because if its small fruit. Although it will form a good centre leader shape without too much training, it is slow to get started. It makes up for this by being extremely heavy cropping. Young bush trees have moderate vigour, growth is semi-spreading and plentifully spurred. As a standard tree, White Jersey is only small or medium sized when mature, with a neat, compact head. It is susceptible to mildew. Flowering mid May, Although it seems to be self fertile, it produces little pollen and is not suitable as a pollinator. The juice has an excellent flavour and it is a variety well worth growing as a juice apple.

White jersey apples are usually rather small, golden yellow and conical with a nose. Falling freely in late September to early October

Fruit: Small to medium; 45–55mm. Conical, base rounded; often rather lopsided, slightly angular. Stem fairly fleshy, thick, green, usually projecting slightly from a small, broad, shallow cavity. Eye basin slight, or small and shallow, eye usually fairly smooth, sometimes slightly puckered; calyx closed. Skin smooth, dry. Russet often a flash in stem cavity, sometimes a net spreading from eye. Coloured primrose yellow, flush absent. Flesh medium to full bittersweet; juicy; chewy; pale yellowish.

Juice: SG 1051; acidity 0.29%; tannin 0.26%

Cider: The good quality juice of White Jersey is sweet and astringent, producing a dry, rather bitter cider which is useful for extending.

WINTER STUBBARD

Late Bittersweet

Rather uncommon still but occurring as single trees in parts of West Dorset and East Devon, Winter Stubbard makes a spreading, weeping tree that crops rather biennially. Our young trees for the DATA Project were very tall and had almost no feathers in the nursery [Distributed 2011]. Their leaves were very large and round with broadly serrate margins. This variety flowers mid season but is not ready until late October and keeps well.

The knobbly green fruit are closely clustered on the branches. Each has indistinct ribs rising to a very bumpy, crowned, pinched and puckered nose.

Fruit: Medium to large, 45–60mm. Conical with a broad base and a small pinched nose; often lopsided, with 5 or 10 indistinct ribs. Stem long [15–20mm], projecting distinctly from a deep, heavily gold russeted cavity. Eye basin small, narrow, irregularly 5 or more crowned. Eye closed, sepals short and downy. Skin smooth, slightly waxy, occasionally spreading patches of russet. Lenticels may be black or red on cheek. Colour Bramley green, usually without a flush but occasionally a trace of yellow on one side. Flesh mild culinary sharp, sweet with slight astringency; chewy, greenish, browning rapidly.

Juice: SG 1046; acidity 0.23%; tannin 0.45%

Cider: Rather astringent and thin. Sugar content often low.

WOODBINE

Late Sweet Cider Apple

Synonym: Runaway, Rice's Jersey [Glastonbury district]

Found throughout Somerset, Devon and Dorset where it is still popular in traditional orchards, Woodbine is one of a group of similar apples, all vigorous trees with sweet tasting fruit producing cider with a curious woody after-taste. Woodbine is often said to be the same as Slack-ma-Girdle. They are both distinct although it is sometimes only possible to tell them apart by looking at the tree habit. Woodbine forms an open tree with a few long, spreading limbs. Slack-ma-Girdle is more compact with numerous limbs. There is also an Improved Woodbine which looks similar to the parent, but is very susceptible to scab and has little to recommend it.

Woodbine is very fast growing and was often used as a stem and framework tree in the Glastonbury to Shepton Mallet area were it is still known as Rice's Jersey. As for its other name, Runaway – although it makes a useful if rather alternative flavoured cider, its effects on the digestive system have earned it a similar medicinal reputation to Slack-ma-Girdle!

Woodbine fruits are medium sized, flattened and two thirds covered with a distinctive rosy-red striped flush, speckled with small brown dots. Maturing mid-late October.

Fruit: Medium to large; 45–more than 60mm. Oblate; often lopsided, somewhat angular tending to ribbed. Stem thick stub, sometimes strigged or with bulge at spur end, projecting slightly or within a rather deep cavity. Eye basin medium, often broad and deep; irregular tending to crowned, often deformed by scab; calyx open or closed, sepals often free, upright, green. Skin smooth and dry; lenticels as small brown dots. Scab susceptible. Coloured green to yellow-green, always, 25–75% flecked and striped, pinkish-red to greyish-mauve. Flesh sweet; chewy; greenish, vascular strands green.

Juice: SG 1051; acidity 0.2%; tannin 0.12%

Cider: Woodbine cider is rather lacking in character, but has a pleasant, curiously woody flavour. It is useful for blending. Fermentation is slow to medium.

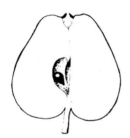

YARLINGTON MILL

Late Mid Season Bittersweet Cider Apple

This genuine Somerset 'jersey' apple was found as a 'gribble' growing out of the wall of the tail race of the mill at Yarlington near North Cadbury by a miller Edward Bartlett in the late 19th century. His son planted it in the garden to use it as a stock, but when in due course it bore good, bittersweet apples that made a fair cider, it was kept and named Yarlington Mill. It was propagated by nurseryman Harry Masters and became very popular by late 19th Century. In the middle of the 20th Century it was reintroduced and used widely for head working unproductive varieties. Later, in the 1970s, it was chosen for many bush orchards planted by Taunton Cider Company, where it constitutes about 15% of the acreage. Yarlington Mill continues to prove very popular and is still propagated and planted enthusiastically, both as a bush and a standard tree. It grows in many areas of the West Country where it invariably performs reliably, but rather biennially, under widely different conditions.

A mature standard tree is medium sized with an upright habit which tends to become spreading. Its leaves are distinctively large, rounded and dark shiny green. Young bush trees have plentiful, sparingly spurred, much branching laterals, which droop under the crop. It is not an easy variety to maintain a good centre leader. Precocious and heavy cropping, if rather biennial, Yarlington Mill responds well to pruning to keep its cropping more regular. It is moderately susceptible to scab on both leaves and fruit. Flowering time is early mid season.

Yarlington fruit can often be quite large, conical with a distinct nose, yellow with a pinkish flush. Maturing by late October to early November.

Fruit: Medium to large; 50–more than 60mm. Conical, sometimes tending to cylindrical; base flat, nose distinct. Stem projecting slightly, sometimes level with the base; cavity wide, deep. Eye basin rather small, puckered; calyx usually slightly open, sepals short. Skin smooth, slightly waxy, russet usually confined to stem cavity; lenticels inconspicuous. Scab susceptible. Colour yellow or greenish-yellow, usually about 65% flushed and slightly striped or flecked dark red with paler background. Flesh sweet with some astringency; white, frequently reddened under flush, slightly crisp.

Juice: SG 1052; acidity 0.22%; tannin 0.32%

Cider: Yarlington Mill's medium bittersweet juice is good and makes a pleasant tasting cider with an agreeable aroma.

YEOVIL SOUR

Late Medium Sharp Cider Apple

Synonym: Sour Cadbury

Yeovil Sour was first mentioned as a bittersharp in the *History of Somerset* in 1830. The fruit came to Long Ashton early in the 20th Century and was called Yeovil Sour from Martock and Sour Cadbury from Woolston in the south west corner of Somerset, not far from Yeovil. It was recorded by Prof. Barker in his list of *Vintage varieties recommended for planting*. It still occurs in the remnants of old orchards in those areas and occasionally in north Dorset, even as far east as Shaftsbury. Yeovil Sour trees are moderately vigorous, upright and spreading. Flowering is mid-season to late May and crops were recorded as, heavy but biennial.

Yeovil Sour is a late maturing apple. Its smallish conical fruit with pink flushed cheeks are not ready until November.

Fruit: Small to medium; 40–55mm. Flattened conical, base broad and flat, nose broad; regular, tending to ribbed. Stem very short; within a small shallow cavity. Eye basin small, smooth, regular; calyx usually closed, often slightly open. Skin rough, dry; covered with a network of fine patchy russet especially associated with lenticels. Coloured pale yellow, usually less than 50% flushed diffuse pinkish-orange. Flesh sharp.

Juice: SG 1052; acidity 0.55%; tannin 0.15%

Cider: Yeovil Sour cider has been described as medium brisk with an attractive character in favourable seasons, but usually best blended. It is medium sharp and the sugar content is often above average.

TEN OF THE BEST NEW 21ST CENTURY CIDER APPLE SELECTIONS

[NB. 1.0 g/l ≡ 0.10% tannin]

These are the best of the new selections coming from the Long Ashton breeding program for early maturing cider apples in the late 1990s. They have steadily grown in popularity and these ten varieties have been the most planted in the last few years since they were launched. The following nineteen varieties, although they have been less popular, are equally good and suitable for a wide range of locations and orchard conditions. The juice analysis figures given are from fruit collected from young trees, so it is expected that the sugar and tannin levels will improve as the trees mature.

ANGELA
New Mild Bittersharp Cider Apple

Nursery number: 11/82
[Named after Angela Berrie, plant pathologist from East Malling Research. Kent]
Angela has proved a popular choice for its compact growth habit suited to intensive planting or small spaces and also

for its well flavoured juice. Trees have moderate vigour and form a good natural centre leader. Flowering early May. Ready late September-early October.

The heavy, bright red glossy fruits often have a distinctively off-set stem with a bulge at the base.

Fruit: Large, 55–>60mm. Conical, base rounded; lopsided, tending to ribbed. Stem thick fleshy, often with a bulge at the base, projecting slightly from a small cavity. Eye basin small, shallow but rather irregular, crowned and beaded. Eye usually closed. Skin dry. Lenticels occasionally russeted or with a pale surround on the flush. Slight specking of russet frequent. Colour yellow-green, always more than half covered with a strong diffuse dark red flush, often flecked with heavy maroon. Flesh chewy, greenish.

Juice: Well flavoured bittersharp, often pink.
SG 1045; malic 0.62%; tannin 1.9g/l

FIONA

New Mild Bittersharp Cider Apple

Nursery number: 11/90

Fiona is now proving a useful and well behaved variety producing good, regular crops of large fruit. An excellent, compact tree with light weight branches and a strong natural centre leader, Fiona is useful for intensive planting but would benefit from a strong rootstock on open sites. Slightly susceptible to mildew but proving scab free so far. Flowering early May and maturing early-mid September.

The good sized conical yellow fruits, always have a pinkish-orange flush on the cheek.

Fruit: Medium-large, 50–60mm. Flattened conical, tending to oblate, nose broad and base flattened; slightly angular or regularly ribbed. Stem usually projecting slightly from a small cavity lined with golden russet. [12–15mm]. Eye basin very slight, tending to crowned. Eye more or less closed. Skin smooth, dry. Lenticels often conspicuous with a pale surround. Colour yellow-green sometimes less than one third covered with a slight brownish-orange or pinkish flush. Flesh sharp, juicy, greenish.

Juice: Slightly sweet, acidic but lacking body.
SG 1049; malic 0.69%; tannin 1.5g/l

GILLY

New Mild Bittersharp Cider Apple

Nursery number: 11/58

[Named after Gilly Turner, indispensable p.a. in Bulmers Fruit Office]

Gilly has been a popular choice for planting recently up in Herefordshire. It makes a very good small to medium sized tree with light weight branches but it is only moderately vigorous and tends to run out of steam if allowed to crop too heavily when young. Flowering early May and ready to harvest by mid September.

The rounded red and yellow fruits have a distinct 'Worcester' aroma and a characteristic hammered surface.

Fruit: Medium large, 50–60mm. Flattened conical, tending to cylindrical; slightly ribbed. Stem long 15mm], projecting distinctly from a narrow but deep cavity. Eye basin small, shallow, smooth, beaded surround. Eye closed. Skin shiny, greasy, surface hammered. Light russet in stem cavity. Colour: pale yellow-green, always more than two thirds covered with a strong diffuse bright red flush, striped and flecked dark red. Flesh well flavoured, sweet, juicy, melting, yellowish.

Juice: Sweet, acidic and slightly farmyardy [distinct blend of tannins] SG 1053; malic 0.54%; tannin 1.8g/l

HASTINGS

New Bittersweet Cider Apple

Nursery number: 10/66

[So named for its nursery number]

One of the best of the new selections Hastings has become a popular choice. It gives good regular crops of large fruit well distributed on an excellent small tree. It has moderate vigour so care has to be taken to keep the leader growing strongly when the trees are young but they respond well to hearty nitrate feeding. Hastings can be susceptible to potash deficiency. Flowering mid May and ready by mid September.

The red and yellow striped and spotted fruits are distinctly flattened with a broad nose and a long stem.

Fruit: Large 55–>60mm. Rather flattened conical or oblate; more or less rounded. Stem long [12–15mm], projecting distinctly from a deep, russeted cavity. Eye basin shallow, slightly puckered, showing ten bumps. Eye closed. Skin smooth, greasy.

Lenticels with a conspicuous pale surround on flush. Colour primrose yellow, always more than two thirds covered with strong bright red flush. Occasionally thinner diffuse flush shows stripes more distinctly. Flesh well flavoured mild bittersweet, juicy, chewy, yellowish.

Juice: Astringent, sweet and slightly acidic.
SG 1057; malic 0.13%; tannin 2.9g/l

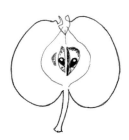

HELENS APPLE

New Bittersweet Cider Apple

Nursery number: 10b/27

[Widely planted for Helen Thomas at Westons Cider]
Helens Apple has earned a reputation for scab resistance making it a popular choice for 'organic' growing. With above average vigour, it forms a strong rather upright tree usually with plentiful spurring. Flowering very early May, sometimes the end of April, it is a useful early pollinator for Three Counties, a sister selection. Helens Apple matures late September to early October.

The large rounded fruits that resemble Dabinett, often have an off-set stem and a speckled orange-crimson flush.

Fruit: Medium-large, 50–60mm. Conical, tending to cylindrical with pointed nose and rounded base; rather irregular, ribbed. Stem fairly long [15–20mm], often off-set, projecting distinctly from a deep, rather russeted cavity. Eye small, shallow, irregularly crowned or puckered, beaded; eye more or less open, sepals green. Skin smooth, waxy. Colour yellow-green ripening to golden yellow, usually flushed, variably from a trace to more than half covered, with dark red flecks over lighter red, similar to Dabinett. Flesh good medium bittersweet, dry, chewy, greenish, browning rapidly.

Juice: Smooth, sweet and astringent with low acidity.
SG 1043; malic 0.10%; tannin 2.9g/l

LIZZY

New Bittersweet Cider Apple

Nursery number: 13/15

[Named after Liz Copas who with a little help, raised and selected the collection]
A reliably cropping variety, Lizzy forms an excellent small tree, amenable, compact and with a good natural centre

leader. Branches are rather upright at first but come down with the first crop. This selection is proving popular and ideal for small spaces or for intensive planting. Flowering very early May.

The pale yellow fruits resemble Michelin its parent, but the resemblance stops there. The fruits will be fully ripe and shakeable by mid September.

Fruit: Medium-large, 55–>60mm. Conical, base broadly rounded; sometimes lopsided. Stem projecting slightly, sometimes more distinctly, from a deep, narrow slightly russeted cavity. [15–17mm]. Eye basin narrow, shallow, rather irregular, tending to beaded. Eye closed, sepals long, green. Skin smooth, dry. Occasional russet patches on the cheeks. Colour yellow-green ripening to pale lemon yellow, frequently with a trace of diffuse brownish-orange flush. Flesh sweet, chewy, greenish.

Juice: Astringent, smooth, low acid with a slight farmyard aroma.
SG 1047; malic 0.17%; tannin 2.0g/l [interesting tannins]

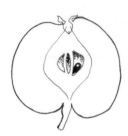

PRINCE WILLIAM

New Bittersweet Cider Apple

Nursery number: 5/18

Prince William forms an excellent small, moderately vigorous tree with a good natural centre leader and well spurred branches. It benefits from a strong rootstock on poor sites but seems to crop heavily and reliably. Flowering very early, in late April in some years or very early May, it could be frost susceptible. Its sister selections, Helens Apple and Three Counties make good pollinators.

The red and yellow striped cylindrical fruits have a characteristically long stem and a rather woody texture. Maturing late September or early October

Fruit: Small-medium, 45–55mm. Rather cylindrical, rounded nose and base; rounded in section. Stem fairly long, [15–18mm], projecting distinctly from a small, deep cavity. Eye basin none or very slight, smooth or slightly crowned. Sepals long, green reflexed. Skin smooth, dry. Colour green, always more than three quarters covered with a colourful pink flush, lightly striped bright red. Flesh mild bittersweet, chewy, melting, yellowish.

Juice: Sweet, slightly astringent but rather thin.
SG 1057; malic 0.15%; tannin 2.5g/l

THREE COUNTIES

New Bittersweet Cider Apple

Nursery number: 11/9

An excellent tree, fairly vigorous with a good strong natural centre leader. Although rather sparsely spurred it produces good, regular crops and has become a popular choice for an early maturing apple. Can run out of steam if allowed to over crop in its youth. Flowering early May and makes a good pollinator for Helens Apple.

The rounded red fruits mature mid-late September and look very similar to Dabinett.

Fruit: Large, 50->60mm. Conical with a broad nose and rounded base; tending to ribbed, sometimes rather lopsided. Stem quite long [15–18mm], projecting distinctly from a narrow, deep, sometimes heavily russeted cavity. Eye basin none or very slight, occasionally beaded, usually smooth but tending to be crowned. Eye usually closed, sepals green. Skin smooth, dry. Lenticels on the flush have a pale surround. Colour: Green or greenish-yellow, always over half covered with a diffuse, strongly flecked dark crimson flush, similar to Dabinett. Flesh sweet with a trace of tannin, chewy, greenish.

Juice: Sweet, low acid with a robust astringency.
SG 1057; malic 0.20%; tannin 3.0g/l

VICKY

New Bittersweet Cider Apple

Nursery number: 6/7

[Named after Vicky Child who helped make the original pollinations and sections]

Vicky makes a very nice tree of moderate size and strong vigour, a popular choice for exposed or difficult sites. It can be scab susceptible. Flowering late April or early May, frosty site should be avoided. Maturing mid September.

The large, attractive, bright red, shiny, often lopsided fruits have a distinctly projecting often off-set stem.

Fruit: Large-very large, 55->60mm. Flattened conical to cylindrical with a rounded nose and broad base; roundly ribbed in section. Stem fairly long [15 – 18mm], often off-set and with a bulge at the base, projecting distinctly from a large, deep, russeted cavity. Eye basin variable, often shallow, tending to be puckered or furrowed, slightly crowned. Eye more or less open, sepals long, green. Skin smooth, shiny, waxy turning greasy. Lenticels with a conspicuous pale surround on the flush. Colour pale mottled yellow, always more than half or two thirds covered with a bright red diffuse flush, strongly speckled and striped with darker red. Flesh good dessert flavoured, sharp, sweet, crisp or slightly chewy, melting, yellowish, reddened under the skin.

Juice: Slightly astringent, low acid, sweet and often pink.
SG 1049; malic 0.15%; tannin 1.4g/l

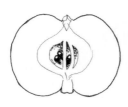

WILLY

New Bittersharp Cider Apple

Nursery number: 9/69

[Named after Ray Williams, Cider Pomologist for many years at Long Ashton and whose brainchild the breeding program was]

Willy makes an excellent lightweight tree with a good natural centre leader. It may need a strong rootstock on heavy sites. It has a similar growth habit to Dabinett its parent. It can be slightly susceptible to mildew. Flowering often very early in May, it is not suitable for sites prone to late frosts. Willy matures very early and begins to drop mid-late September.

The large rounded barrel-shaped yellow fruits have a characteristic stem that is often shaped into a tail.

Fruit: Large, 55–>60mm. Flattened cylindrical with a broad nose and rounded base; angular and roundly ribbed in section. Stem usually a stub with the cavity or projecting slightly, often strigged or off-set. Cavity small but deep and with a little russet. Eye basin slight or non existent, usually clearly beaded. Sepals reflexed and eye closed. Skin smooth, waxy becoming greasy. Lenticels often small brown dots on the flush only. Colour pale yellow-green ripening to golden yellow, often with a light patch of pink and the occasional stripe. Flesh good flavoured sharp with some tannin, melting, cream coloured.

Juice: Acidic, slightly astringent, fresh and sweet.
SG 1052; malic 0.68%; tannin 1.9g/l

A FURTHER 19 GOOD
NEW SELECTIONS

AMANDA [5/14]

[Grand-daughter to Liz Copas]

A good Golden Delicious style tree but with large Michelin-like fruit. A tip bearer with good branch angles and a good centre leader but can be vigorous with some bare wood and possibly too many laterals. Leaves rather folded and upright. Flowers early May.

Fruit: A good flavoured woody textured mild bittersweet, large, tall conical with a long, off-set stem. Skin turning golden yellow with a slight orange-pink flush. Maturing mid-late September.

Juice: Sweet and astringent with a faint farmyard aroma. Slightly pink hue.
SG 1.053; acidity 0.22%; tannin 0.23%

AMELIA [2/25]

Rather variable on the growers' trial sites but usually a fairly good, smallish and heavily spurred tree with a good centre leader. A tip-bearing Michelin x James Grieve cross that crops well. Slightly susceptible to scab and blossom wilt. Flowers mid May.

Fruit: Large, turning pale yellow with a slight pink flush, a rather ribbed conical shape with long green sepals and a long stem. A chewy textured good bittersweet. Dropping late September-early October.

Juice: Straw coloured. Sweet and astringent, no acidity. Aroma plain.
SG 1.059; acidity 0.19%; tannin 0.27%

CONNIE [11/192]

[Named after Liz's mother]

Good tree with good strong vigour and plentiful well spurred laterals. Its tendency to multiple clusters does not usually affect cropping. May be prone to scab. Flowers early May.

Fruit: Excellent medium sized, tall conical, sometimes almost elliptical, Michelin-like with a small pinched eye. The stem can be variable but is usually long. Skin pale yellow with a trace of pinkish-orange flush. Maturing and shakeable mid September.

Juice: Full bittersweet, deep straw hue.
SG 1.050; acidity 0.17%; tannin 0.23%

SHAMROCK [12/51]

[This one was selected for planting in Ireland]

A good fairly vigorous tree, rather heavily spurred and sometimes rather biennial but usually cropping well. A tip bearer. Moderately susceptible to scab. Flowers rather early in late April. Not suitable to frost prone sites.

Fruit: A very characteristic shape-large, tall conical and rather 'waisted' with a very small nose and broad base. The eye is tiny, beaded and pinched closed. The stem is long, fleshy green and slightly off-set. Skin green ripening to yellow-green with a slight orange flush. A very good sharp flavoured fruit with a chewy texture and ready mid-late September.

Juice: Very acidic and sweet, with low astringency.
SG 1.050; acidity 1.11%; tannin 0.14%

TRACEY [6/20]

A very good, small, lightweight tree useful for intensive planting. This selection may need extra care on some poorer sites to maintain annual cropping. Can be very mildew susceptible. Tracey is a good flavoured sharp juice apple, large, flattened-conical, with a stub of a stem and a slightly open eye with upright sepals. Skin green ripening to butter yellow with light, brownish-red flecked and striped flush. Shaking late September. Flowering late April-early May.

Juice: Good, acidic with a slight floral aroma. Slight pink hue
SG 1.051; acidity 0.61%; tannin 0.20%

JANE [11/56]
A good moderately vigorous tree, with a rather weak leader that would benefit from a stronger rootstock on many sites. A tip bearer with numerous moderately spurred laterals at good angles. Fruit large, conical-cylindrical with a broad rounded base and broad often beaded nose. Stem long and often off-set. Skin ripening to a dirty primrose, well covered with a heavy crimson Worcester flush, lenticels conspicuous in a pale surround. Maturing late September Flowering mid May.

Juice: Sweet and astringent with slightly farmyardy aroma. Deep straw hue.
SG 1.052; acidity 0.19%; tannin 0.33%

MARGARET [8/14]
[Named after Margaret Worle]

A good small tree that sometimes can be rather weak. May need extra care and encouragement on poorer sites to maintain annual cropping. Some slight scab and mildew. Flowers early so not suitable for a frosty site. Fruit large, rounded flattened cylindrical with a broad shallow eye and a long stem. Skin yellow with broad rosy pink flecks over a diffuse crimson flush. Flesh often reddened and with a melting texture. Very early maturing, dropping early September. Flowers early in late April.

Juice: Mild, juicy bittersharp, well flavoured and pink.
SG 1.050; sugar 12.7%; tannin 0.28%

SALLY [11/122]
A very good shaped tree, medium sized but with good vigour. But it may need care to sustain vigour to maintain annual cropping. Occasionally succumbs to

severe scab. Fruit medium sized, rounded conical-cylindrical with a long stem and an open eye. The core is hollow and the flesh often stained red. Skin greenish yellow with a heavy dark striped Worcester flush. Shakeable mid September. Flowering end April. Not suitable for sites prone to late frosts.

Juice: Bittersweet, slightly farmyardy. Slight rose pink hue.
SG 1.052; acidity 0.58%; tannin 0.14%

TINA [11/167]

A good, very early, full bittersweet, well suited to close intensive planting. A good tree but weak Dabinett cross that may need extra vigour of MM111 on some sites to maintain annual cropping. Plentiful well spurred, rather spreading, whippy laterals at good angles but the leader may be weak and frequently breaks with the weight of fruit. It is best to remove the fruit from the leader of young trees. Fruit large, broadly conical with a shallow beaded eye. Stem often off-set. Skin yellow with slight flush of dark red strips over scarlet. Prone to rotting if not collected soon after falling. Maturing early-mid September. Flowering early May.

Juice: Sweet and astringent. Straw coloured
SG 1.055; acidity 0.18%; tannin 0.25%

JOANNA [4/21]

A very nice tree but can variable depending on the site. Rather too strong in Devon where the weather often encourages leaf at the expense of crop. Joanna benefits from some early removal of excess branches. It can be susceptible to scab, which may show as 'pin' spots on the fruit. Fruit medium to large, conical-cylindrical with a broad nose and a smooth shallow eye. The stem is short, green, fleshy, off-set and just showing. Skin is pale yellow rarely with a little pink flush, but sometimes with russet on the cheek. Maturing mid September. Flowering early May.

Juice: Good, sweet and medium sharp with some tannin. Water white with very little colour.
SG 1.045; acidity 1.15%; tannin 0.22%

HANNAH [8/36]

A fairly small, moderately vigorous tree. It carries many good laterals at a good angle to the trunk but often with unwanted bare wood. The leader can be weak and whippy and it is essential to remove all competitive shoots. Although this selection carries good crops it could go biennial if it is allowed to over-crop and loose momentum. Fruit medium sized, Dabinett-like, conical with a broad crowned and beaded nose and a flat base. Short thick stem. Skin yellow-green with a strong dark red diffuse flush, almost black on some fruits. Flesh full bittersweet, chewy and often reddened under the skin. Maturing mid-late September. Flowering early May.

Juice: Astringent, thin, slight sweetness. Rose pink hue.
SG 1.050; acidity 0.55%; tannin 0.34%

JENNY [8/45]

Good tree but rather small and slow to start cropping. Rather weak and possibly better on MM111. Fruit, medium large, rounded conical-cylindrical with a small puckered and beaded eye, and a long stem. Skin turning primrose yellow with much Worcester-like maroon flush, and thin crimson stripes, lenticels surrounded with yellow spots. Flesh reddened beneath the skin and with a pleasant aroma. Ready early September. Flowering early May.

Juice: Deep russet pink and pleasantly full bittersweet.
SG 1.046; acidity 0.07%; tannin 0.25%

NAOMI [8/55]

Good tree with good leader but strong growing and tending to be rather upright with some bare wood. Fruit large, broadly conical-cylindrical, Dabinett shaped with James Grieve colouring, pale yellow-green turning golden with flecked and striped crimson flush. Stem long and eye with upright sepals. Ready mid-late September. Flowering late April.

Juice: Astringent, smooth, low acid and sweet with a floral aroma. Rose pink hue.
SG 1.041; acidity 0.28%; tannin 0.17%

NICKY [10b/7]

A very good tree but can be rather weak on MM106. May need care on some sites to maintain annual cropping. Mildew and scab susceptible. Fruit rather small, rounded, conical-cylindrical with a long stem and broadly crowned open eye with upright sepals. Skin a warm yellow with light bright orange-red striped shiny, greasy flush. Ready early-mid September. Flowering late April-early May.

Juice: Acidic with some astringency and background sweetness. Straw coloured. SG 1.048; acidity 0.40%; tannin 0.17%

BETTY [11/52]

A good, light-weight but well spurred tree with a rather weak leader. May need care to sustain vigour to maintain annual cropping. Sometimes prone to canker. Fruit a good flavoured, crisp, sweet, juicing sharp. Large cylindrical shape with a broad nose and small rounded base. A long stalk projects distinctly. Eye basin small but deep, with long green upright sepals. Skin ripening to primrose yellow with a blush of a slightly darker golden yellow. Dropping mid-late September. Flowers mid May.

Juice: Farmyard aroma and flavour [Bramley-like] SG 1.050; acidity 0.90%; tannin 0.11%

ELENI [11/38]

A moderately vigorous tree with a strong natural centre leader. Its numerous rather whippy laterals grow out at good angles to the trunk and are well spurred with many dards. Sometimes prone to canker. Fruit medium sized, rounded conical with distinct ribs and a broadly crowned nose. Stem long and projecting from a deep cavity. Skin ripening golden yellow with a slight speckled brownish-orange flush. Maturing mid September. Flowering early May.

Juice: Good flavour with a rather farmyardy aroma but lacks astringency. SG 1.047; acidity 0.98%; tannin 0.17%

DEBBIE [12/47]

A very good healthy, easy to manage tree with reasonable vigour. Not quick to come into cropping but likely to be regular. Good crops of very large, crisp textured Greensleeves-like fruit. Fruit large, rounded cylindrical with a broad flat nose and a long stem. Skin green ripening to golden yellow sometimes with a little orange flush. Mature and dropping early-mid September. Flowers mid May.

Juice: Acidic with slight astringency, fresh with a background sweetness.
SG 1.050; acidity 0.97%; tannin 0.12%

EARLY BIRD [12/171]

The most early maturing selection, maturing and dropping early September, shakeable some years in late August. Excellent tree with good vigour, strong leader, rather too many well spurred laterals that would benefit from early selecting out. Its tendency to hold its fruit in clusters might mean that it will eventually go biennial. Fruit medium sized, slightly waisted conical Michelin-like with a stubby stem. Skin yellow without any flush. Flesh chewy textured. Maturing and dropping early September. Flowers early May.

Juice: Astringent, slightly bitter, medium sweet and fresh. Straw coloured
SG 1.055; acidity 0.21%; tannin 0.55%

JEAN [11/66]

[Named after Ray William's wife]

Rather a small tree with slightly weak Dabinett-like leader, but plentiful laterals at acceptable angles to the trunk. May need care on some sites to maintain annual and prevent over-cropping. Fruit medium to large, flattened and rounded conical with a short-ish stem projecting slightly from a deep cavity. Skin greenish yellow, part covered with a mottled orange flush. Lenticels conspicuous in a pale surround. Maturing mid–late September. Flowering mid May.

Juice: Good flavoured bittersweet
SG 1.057; acidity 0.16%; tannin 0.33%

USEFUL NAMES AND ADDRESSES

Tree Nurseries

K. Croucher, Thornhayes Nursery, Nr Cullompton, Devon EX15 2DF
www.thornhayes-nursery.co.uk
Specialist supplier of West Country varieties and cider apples.

John Worle Tree Nursery
www.johnworle.co.uk
Special collection of trees for the artisan and craft cidermaker.
Supplier of the new cider apple selections from Long Ashton.

Endsleigh Gardens, Milton Abbot, Devon PL19 0PG
www.endsleigh-gardens.com
For old Tamar Valley Apples

Adam's Apples – Talaton Plants Ltd, Honiton, Devon
www.adamsappletrees.co.uk
For Devon and Cornish varieties.

Cornish Apple Trees, Nr Truro
www.cornishappletrees.co.uk
For Cornish varieties

Collections of cider apple and other trees

Thatchers Cider Company, Sandford, North Somerset. BS25 5RA
www.thatcherscider.co.uk

National Fruit Collection, Brogdale Road, Faversham, Kent, ME13 8XZ
www.nationalfruitcollection.org.uk

National Trust
www.nationaltrust.org.uk
Several National Trust places have orchards containing local varieties. The one at Cothele near Plymouth has an excellent collection of Cornish apple varieties.

The Orchard Marketplace
www.orchardmarketplace.org.uk
Is an online marketplace run by the Gloucestershire Orchard Group, set up to facilitate the exchange of fruit and other orchard related produce nationwide.

Devon Apples
www.devonapples.co.uk
A directory of Devon and other West Country apples – complete with more photos for identification purposes.

Cornwall County Council
www.cornwall.gov.uk
List of county apple varieties, their suppliers and much more.

Orchards Live and Orchard Link
www.orchardslive.org.uk and www.orchardlink.org.uk
Two organisations 'Saving orchards in North and South Devon'

Common Ground
www.england-in-particular.info

South West of England Cidermakers Association
www.sweca.org.uk
Worth joining if you are making cider to sell.

Royal Bath & West Show
www.bathandwest.com
And bring your cider to the Annual Cider Competition.

VARIOUS BOOKS

Craft Cider Making
Andrew Lea. The Good Life Press
ISBN 978-1-904871-37-8

Making Craft Cider, A Ciderist's Guide
Simon McKie. Shire Library
ISBN 978-0-74780-817-6

Ciderland
James Crowden. Birlinn Ltd
ISBN 978 -1-84158-627-4
and available from the author www.james-crowden.co.uk

The Fruit Tree Handbook
Ben Pike. Green Books
ISBN 978-1-900322-74-4

Cider Apple Growers Guide 2ⁿᵈ Edition
Liz Copas for the National Association of Cider Makers
ISBN 978-0-9568994-0-8

The Common Ground Book of Orchards
Published by Common Ground
ISBN 1-870364-21-X

The Book of Apples Joan Morgan and Alison Richards
In association with the Brogdale Horticultural Trust.
ISBN 0091883989

The Apple Book
Rosie Saunders. Royal Horticultural Society
ISBN 978-0-7112-3141-2

A Somerset Pomona
Liz Copas
ISBN 1-874336-87-3. Now out of print.

National Apple Register of the UK
Muriel Smith, National Fruit Trials 1971. Now out of print.

Burcombes, Queenies and Colloggetts, the makings of a Cornish orchard
Virginia Spiers.
Published by West Brendon, Cornwall 1996
ISBN 0-9527641-05

Apples: A Guide To The Identification Of International Varieties
John Bultitude
ISBN 0333349717. Now out of print

The Fruit Manual. Robert Hogg [1884]
Reprinted in Limited Edition by Langford Press 2002
ISBN 1-904078-08-7

The Apple and Pear as Vintage Fruits
Robert Hogg [1886]